Decentralization in Management Systems

Ohio State University Press

WILLIAM T. MORRIS

Decentralization in Management Systems

An Introduction to Design

Preface

The question of the proper degree of decentralization or delegation in large organizations is a very old one. As is often the case, however, antiquity alone does not necessarily imply that the answers that have been given to it are satisfactory. Patterns of decentralization have evolved and been tested as organizations have grown. Effective patterns have survived, but the evolutionary process has been a costly one. Through years of casual experimentation first approximation answers have emerged, and recently there have begun to be systematic statements of what these answers are. Yet there appears to be little in the way of carefully stated operational theory on which controlled experiments in the improvement of organizational design might be based. The appearance of organizations that seem to cycle back and forth between relatively high degrees of centralization and decentralization suggests the costliness of casual experimentation. Without some understanding of the basic relationships, further improvements in the design of such large organization must continue to be haphazard.

It is surely needless to call attention to the proliferation of large organizations of all sorts and the obvious importance of the problems of decentralization in these organizations. The advent of on-line, real-time data-processing systems, seen by many as the next significant trend in management, is forcing explicit attention upon these questions. While data-processing systems contribute to the growth of organizations, they also force a careful examination of the entire system and philosophy of management. In order to assimilate such a system, a firm must be very explicit about the degree of centralization or decentralization of decision-making it wishes to achieve. These events, coupled with the developing capabilities of management science in the direction of system or organization design, have motivated this examination of the fundamental question of decentralization.

In what follows we have tried to bring together some of the evidence that bears more or less directly on the question of decentralization in the design and management of large organizations. With this evidence, the attempt is made to develop a theory or hypotheses that will ultimately capture and "explain" some of the important aspects of what is observed in practice; suggest the relevant questions that need to be asked about decentralization; and give those who work in these organizations some additional sensitivity to their environment.

Science proceeds by alternately raising hypotheses and resorting to experimentation, leading only to more hypotheses. Management science proceeds through this empirical-theoretical cycle as well, and the present discussion can best be viewed as an attempt to raise hypotheses out of the available data in anticipation of further experiments. Because these experiments are likely to be very expensive, some care seems to be warranted in developing the hypotheses on which they are to be founded. The purpose then, is to raise hypotheses that may be used to transform casual experience into careful experiment. Although the discussion refers to "system design" and organizational design from time to time, this is not to naïvely suppose that someone sits down at the drawing board and draws the plans for an organization that will suddenly spring into being. Organizations as we know them evolve, and the realistic question for the organizational designer is, "To the extent that one can exert some small influence upon the process of organizational evolution, in which directions should this process be nudged?" In other words, if evolution is a series of small experiments, what experiments should deliberately be undertaken?

Models play a central role in this process of trying to raise useful hypotheses, and it is perhaps worthwhile to be explicit about just what this role is taken to be. It has several aspects.

1. Models are regarded as being essentially devices for increasing understanding. Thus the attributes of simplicity and transparency may be sought in one's models. To capture the full complexity of reality may be less important than to recognize that the basis of human learning is simplification and abstraction.

2. No model is to be regarded as a *fait accompli*. Rather, it is simply a starting point from which one may enrich, complicate, and revise in order to understand particular situations. The models that follow are rather simple and very much to be considered beginnings. The reader will immediately notice that by resorting to simulation one could deal with vastly more complex problems, freed entirely from the cumbersome details of analysis. The price, however, is the loss of much of the transparency and power to give insight that we are presently seeking.

3. The models considered here reflect only the very gross effects observed in actual organizations, and thus the predictions they yield are of a similarly gross nature. We are concerned with what will increase and what will decrease if a particular policy is implemented, not with how much or at what rate the changes will occur.

4. A model is taken here to be essentially a laboratory animal. As a rat is not a man, the model is not the organization. Yet we can do things to the model that we cannot do to the organization. The basic hope is that the things that happen in the model will lead to asking the useful questions about the organization.

This book may be described as a second-level discussion in management science in two senses. First, it supposes that the reader has an elementary acquaintance with such topics as calculus, probability theory, Bayesian statistics, capital budgeting, inventory theory, and waiting-line theory. It attempts to use these ideas rather than introduce them. For the reader who is so inclined, we have tried to make it possible to avoid the analysis entirely. That is, where possible the details of the models have been separated from the insights and hypotheses they suggest. Thus one may consider the latter without being forced into the complexities of the former.

Second, the discussion attempts, however haltingly, to use analysis in the way in which it functions in other sciences. It has sometimes appeared that we have regarded models as tools for solving specific problems and only very remotely connected with our knowledge of management. If we take our ultimate aim to be the accumulation of a body of organized understanding of management phenomena, then analysis is simply a tool toward this end. The prolonged tendency to teach analysis for problem-solving has contributed little to the satisfaction of our curiosity about management and organizational phenomena.

I am indebted to a number of graduate students who worked with me on various aspects of decentralization and especially to S. Sherman Clark and Michael Bommer. Dr. David F. Baker, chairman of Ohio State's Department of Industrial Engineering, arranged for support in a variety of forms, thus preventing the work from falling victim to the pressure of other activities.

W. T. M.

Table of Contents

CHAPTER 1

FROM DATA TO DESIGN

Crisis and Response

William C. Durant, founder of the General Motors Corporation, was confident of the great potential market for the automobile and was convinced that the way to exploit this potential was to bring together a group of existing companies already producing and marketing in the automotive field. He was most successful in carrying out this plan, and by 1919 had built General Motors into the fifth largest industrial enterprise in the United States. Trouble lay ahead, however. Durant, the great builder, had little interest in the problem of making explicit the organization structure of his firm or in developing administrative processes by which to operate it. The excitement of rapid growth for the company together with the increasing revenues from automobile sales diverted his attention from these problems and suppressed the need to face them.

The General Motors Corporation, riding the postwar boom, entered 1920 as a highly decentralized collection of operating companies or divisions. The managers of these divisions, swept along by increasing demand and rising prices for cars, were aggressively expanding their inventories and their plant capacities. Each manager, concerned exclusively with his own division, wanted to protect himself against inflation and shortages by means of a strong inventory position. Continued inability to meet the demand for automobiles impelled each one toward larger and larger capital-investment programs. Although the division managers together constituted the executive committee of the corporation, none of them was concerned with the corporation's problems or with the possibilities of long-term economic movements. Nor was Durant in any better position to take the large view.

The major decisions for each division were made in several ways. Plant expansion, capital investment, production schedules, and prices were sometimes decided by Durant after informal talks with the division managers. Sometimes, the division managers took these things into their own hands, with only the most limited co-ordination with Durant's office. Durant would sometimes authorize a particular capital expenditure during a plant visit without any record of the decision being made. At other times, the executive committee would make capital appropriations; but the members did considerable "horse trading" of the form, "I'll vote for your project if you'll vote for mine." Thus there were no standardized financial procedures, nor was there any method of controlling expenditures. Large over-runs on capital authorizations were the rule. Further, there was virtually nothing in the way of standardized accounting procedures, leaving Durant without any means of measuring and comparing the performance of his divisions.

As the year 1920 wore on into spring, the divisions became increasingly demanding in their requests for capital. Their inventories continued upward. The corporation sought new capital both by borrowing and by the sale of additional common stock. Then, in September the automobile market collapsed, the postwar recession began, and the General Motors Corporation very nearly ceased production. The firm's stock fell; it became more and more difficult for the divisions to meet payrolls and short-term debts; and Durant resigned as president. The new president, Pierre Du Pont, some time before had seen an organization plan for the corporation worked out by Alfred Sloan, head of the parts and accessories division. Almost immediately after becoming president, Du Pont began to implement the Sloan plan. It was perhaps the first lucid design for what we now refer to as a decentralized organization.

Sloan recognized that there was much to be gained by permitting the divisions to have great responsibility for their own operations. On the other hand, there was clearly some need for central control and co-ordination of their operations if the firm was to realize the potential strengths of being large. In the area of capital budgeting, for example, he clearly saw the message of the crisis of 1920. His response was to produce a design in which some smaller investments could be authorized by the division managers, but larger investments had to be submitted to corporate headquarters. At that point a check needed to be made on that data submitted by the divisions in support of their proposals, and a common basis for comparison among proposals was necessary. The headquarters group would have to review each proposal both in the light of the long-term objectives of the corporation and with a long view of the economic outlook. From this vantage point an effective allocation of the corporation's available capital could be made among the divisions. This was to be followed up by controls on the expenditures of funds and by a method of measuring and comparing the over-all financial performance of the divisions. In this way Sloan sought to leave the day-to-day operating responsibilities at the divisional level, whereas long-term decisions and problems of co-ordination among divisions were handled at headquarters. Pervading the whole design were the concepts of clear definition of authority and responsibility and carefully designed systems of information flow to permit effective co-ordination and control.

Sloan's design may be viewed as a well-considered response to a crisis in the evolutionary development of an organization. Other firms approached similar organizational forms from different starting points and by slower evolutionary processes. Of course, the Sloan design itself was only the beginning of an extended period of experimentation in organizational plans, but it did represent a rather complete and well-developed set of hypotheses on which to base such experiments. One might generally characterize the General Motors crisis as the result of excessive decentralization. Other firms, of which Du Pont is a good example, found themselves in difficulty for exactly the opposite reasons. They suffered from excessive centralization. Top managers in these highly centralized, functionally organized firms were unable to meet the twin stimuli of growing national markets and the dramatic enrichment of production and product technologies.[1]

Organizational Growth

Large organizations can be managed not by a single brain but through co-ordinated decisions made by many. Just how decisions are to be thus delegated and the resulting actions co-ordinated is the central question in organization design. It seems clear that since the information-handling and decision-making capacities of the chief executive are finite, the organization must eventually grow beyond the point where he becomes a limiting factor bringing about diminishing returns. Things begin to get out of hand, and the organization is regarded as too big.[2]

As a firm grows, one might imagine the transformation of its internal structure taking place along the following general lines. When the chief executive finds his information-processing and decision-making capacities taxed toward their limit, he delegates some work to subordinates. Thus begins the emergence of an elaborate hierarchy of line managers who come into existence through delegation of the work of managing. This raises immediately the problem of co-ordination. How are the actions and decisions of these managers made compatible, each with the other and with the objectives of the firm as a whole? As the lines of communication multiply and lengthen, the possibilities for delays in decision-making, uncertainty as to what is going on in the firm, and incompatible decisions increase.

As these processes are taking place through delegation, another kind of change emerges. The volume of decisions grows to the point where specialized information and advice to support various classes of decisions are not only required but can easily be justified economically. Thus begins the evolution of staff services within the company to fill these two needs. Some staff services, such as accounting, function chiefly to provide information for co-ordination and control, helping to assure the compatibility of decisions made by various managers within the firm. Other staff services give specialized advice, as in the case of the legal, marketing, or personnel staffs.

Some have been concerned lest the process of delegation lead eventually to such a large and complex hierarchy of line managers that increasing costs of administration per worker and increasing delays in making decisions would result in a firm uneconomical to manage. When the chief executive finds that the number of subordinates who report to him has grown beyond some vaguely defined point of effectiveness, another level in the organizational hierarchy is instituted. This process goes on, increasing the number of levels of management as the size of the organization grows. The number of subordinates reporting to a superior is called the span of control. Both experience and evidence tend to indicate that, contrary to such fears, the growth of line management will not itself create an excessive burden on the organization. If the span of control is kept constant, the number of line managers tends to grow exponentially with the number of levels in the hierarchy, but so also does the number of workers. Thus the ratio of managers to workers tends to remain nearly constant. In the companies studied by Haire, it also appeared that as they grew the span of control tended in fact to increase.[3] In firms having between twenty and fifty employees, the average span of control was 11.5 subordinates per superior. When, however, these firms grew to a size of more than 200 employees, the span of control had increased to 21. Haire also discovered that the percentage of employees in top and middle management dropped over the same growth span from 13.6 per cent to 4.1 per cent. It may well be that in the long run the capacities of top management are not the limiting factor in the growth of the firm.

As the line functions grow, they must, however, be supported by the addition of staff services. How does the staff emerge and grow? Again, the four companies whose histories Haire examined in detail give us the first clues. He defined staff as all those who provide specialized support, advice, and help for line personnel. Line personnel, in turn, includes all those directly concerned with the making and selling of the product. The companies he examined began with nearly everyone falling into the category of line positions. During the first six to ten years in the lives of these companies, the proportion of staff increased very rapidly indeed. At the end of this period, however, the percentage of staff people tends to stabilize—in two of the firms at about 50 per cent, and in the other two at about 25 per cent. If one were to generalize from this, it might be suggested that in the early years the staff will grow geometrically while the line grows linearly; but later, this relation relaxes into one of parallel growth. It is interesting to note that staff employment appears more stable than line employment, remaining quite insensitive to reductions in the work force.

Another study, somewhat differently conceived from that of Haire, has been done by Baker and Davis.[4] They also were interested in the emergence and growth of the staff, but chose to study some 211 companies of various sizes at a single point in time rather than examine the life histories of individual firms. Out of such data came a number of interesting statements. They suggest that every time a firm adds 100 direct workers, the number of indirect workers increases by 75, regardless of the size of the firm before the addition. This agrees in general with the pattern of parallel growth that emerged in the later years of the companies Haire examined.

Accounting tends to grow at the fastest rate, adding about 4.6 people with every addition of 100 direct workers. Personnel grows at a rate of 1.46 staff people added for each 100 new direct workers. Industrial engineering, which Baker and Davis conceive of rather narrowly as time-and-motion study, grows at the rate of 1.10 staff members per 100 direct workers. Some groups of indirect workers such as inspection, cafeteria, maintenance, and engineering, tend to grow at an increasing rate as the number of direct workers grows. As Haire noticed, Baker and Davis show that the number of top-management executives tends to grow at a decreasing rate.

The emergence of various staff functions as differentiated groups in the organization proceeds at varying rates. By the time a firm has from 75 to 99 workers, the functions of accounting, purchasing, and engineering are completely differentiated. Yet production control, time-and-motion study, personnel, and inspection do not emerge until the company has grown into the range of from 100 to 499 employees. In the case of time-and-motion study in particular, 78 per cent of the firms employing less than 300 direct workers either did not have this function or allowed it to remain completely integrated with other functions. Among companies with more than 300 direct employees, time-and-motion study had emerged, and was completely differentiated as an organization entity in 69 per cent of the firms studied.

These studies suggest some useful hypotheses. Apparently, the emergence and early growth of the staff is rather dramatic while the firm is small and young. The staff groups quickly achieve an institutional existence and come to constitute an important portion of the organization. As time passes and the firm grows, the expansion of the staff settles down to a pattern paralleling that of the line or direct employees. At the same time, the number of middle and top managers increases at a decreasing rate, so that this group comes eventually to constitute a smaller portion of the organization.

Haire has suggested that the sorts of changes in form and structure that take place as an organization grows are those necessary to meet and overcome the forces tending to destroy the organization. This principle, drawn from studies of the growth of organisms, suggests that the emergence and growth of the organization's staff functions, in association with, and in response to, delegation, shore up the organization where the need arises. The functions of the staff groups include the gathering and processing of information for decision-making, co-ordination, and control, and furnishing specialized advice in particular fields. Thus the staff is the chief bulwark against lack of communication, conflicting and incompatible decisions, and general disorganization—the potential destructive forces threatening the large firm.

From the negatively accelerated growth of top and middle management one might also draw the conclusion that the staff is an effective means of increasing the abilities and capacities of management. It appears that the staff groups make possible the management of larger firms with relatively fewer managers but without a runaway increase in the size of the staff itself. Clearly, it does not appear that the staff-management hierarchy is going to become a limiting factor in the growth of the firm.

As the firm expands and accommodates itself to the capacities of management through delegation, the need for co-ordination increases. Studies of how executives use their time reveal large portions of it spent in giving and receiving information. Some have supposed the difficulties and costs associated with co-ordinating widely delegated decisions would eventually operate so as to limit the growth of the firm. Admittedly, this is a difficult problem for large management hierarchies, but experience confirms it is by no means an insoluble problem.

When decision-making responsibilities are delegated, responsibilities for co-ordination of decisions at lower levels are delegated as well. Thus the demands of co-ordination placed upon different members of management may be varied by altering the structure of the organization itself. A critical variable in understanding the problems of co-ordination in any organization is the degree of self-containment of the organization's various subunits. When two or more units compete for a share of some common resources, such as the capital budget of the firm, or when the output of one subunit forms the input of another, they cannot be considered highly self-contained. The less the degree of self-containment, the greater the need for detailed co-ordination and control.

An important aspect of the problem of organization design involves making these divisions self-contained to a large extent and thus reducing the burden of co-ordination. The ultimate extension of this line of development, which is often discussed but seldom truly approached in practice, is to permit the divisions to operate as virtually independent business units so that co-ordination will be reduced to a minimum. The trick, of course, is to do this and yet assure that the divisions operate so as to advance the objectives of the firm as a whole.

The evolutionary changes in the design of the subunits of the organization are often thought to proceed along the following lines. When the organization is small, the subunits tend to be formed by grouping similar processes together, as for example in the typical departmentalized manufacturing plant. As the organization grows, however, the advantages obtained from process-organized subunits tend to be outweighed by the increasing costs of co-ordination. The advantage shifts eventually to the organization of subunits according to purpose or end product, thus substantially reducing the need for co-ordination.

Chandler's Analysis

Going beyond the high level generalizations and looking in detail at the process of organizational evolution in individual firms casts light on some of the reasons for the emergence of differing organizational forms. Chandler gives us a detailed analysis of the history of four large companies and then tests his concepts by applying them to some seventy others. His explanation of what he found in these firms proceeds roughly as follows.[5]

The first response to an increasing demand for a firm's output is likely to be growth by vertical integration. The firm seeks economies both through the development of its own channels of distribution and through the ownership of its own sources of supply. A functionally departmentalized organization will be built up with units carrying on the processes of research, engineering, purchasing, personnel, manufacturing, sales, and so on. The activities of these functional departments are highly interdependent, and considerable effort is required to co-ordinate their performance in the face of changes in the firm's market. A central office is created that carries on this co-ordinating task.

As the firm grows, it becomes possible economically to justify specialized service departments that carry on product and market research, devise advertising plans, develop quality standards, design standard accounting systems, and so on. Since some of the work done by these departments can benefit more than one of the other departments, the central office appears the proper place to locate them. The central office also becomes the agency that handles the cash, pays the dividends, and plans future capital expenditures for the firm. The central office makes some attempt to appraise the performance of the various functional departments. This often proves most difficult because it is not always entirely clear how the results achieved by the firm can be related to the activities of any one of the functional departments. However, this form of organization can be made to work tolerably well, and it has been highly developed in many firms.

At this point, having achieved considerable size and amassed a complex of vertically integrated resources, some firms attempt to take advantage of another sort of economy. The resources the firm has are not being fully utilized; thus other activities or products are sought. The first step is to develop a "full line" of products that can be marketed effectively through the firm's existing channels of distribution. Next, and most significantly, comes diversification into quite different product lines. This involves taking on products that utilize existing production facilities and organizational skill but that may serve quite a different market from that previously within the firm's experience. This is a particularly critical move. Expansion and growth in a single line of products call only for increases in the scale of existing methods of operation and co-ordination. Diversification, leading the firm into different markets, creates problems of a new order of complexity. The problems of co-ordinating the activities of the functional departments, not with a single relatively homogeneous group of customers, but with a number of groups whose requirements change in different and unfamiliar ways may be too much for the central office. The burdens of co-ordination become great, greater numbers and varieties of problems come to it for consideration, and the pressure of current operations begins to absorb time needed for long-range planning. Complexity and diversity, not size alone, brought to light the organizational inadequacies. The response of the firm must be a new, or at least a greatly altered, form of organization that can cope with the new diversity of its operations.

One general form of the response is the multidivisional organization, or "decentralized" structure. Each division is capable of carrying the majority of the functions associated with producing a given product line or serving a given market. The division will thus have within its own structure functional units for sales, manufacturing, engineering, and so on. There will, however, be a headquarters organization that may still provide support to the divisions in some function such as research, advertising, or accounting. One of the critical design problems becomes the choice of which functions are to be performed by the divisions and which by the headquarters unit. Perhaps the most important result emerging here is the assignment of long-range planning to headquarters to the exclusion of almost all concern with the day-to-day operating problems of the divisions. Thus headquarters performs the function of responding to long-range changes in market structure by means of research, product development, capital budgeting, adding and eliminating divisions, and so on. The divisions in turn become skilful in responding to the market changes in their own particular areas of activity.

The decentralized structure brought with it several fundamental benefits. As a product- or "result"-oriented organizational structure, it tended to respond both more quickly and more effectively to changes in each division's environment. It became possible for headquarters to consider the long-term problems of the firm quite free from the distractions of its diverse current and routine activities. This was made workable by a greater possibility of appraising the results of a division's activities and a greater logical association between the division's results and the efforts of its management. Thus the divisions tended to become more like independent businesses whose profitability could be clearly discerned. Again, a crucial design problem for the organization is just how independent the divisions should be permitted to become. Too loose a federation of independent activities is also known to be a weak organizational form. By making a clear association between divisional results and the division's management decisions, not only did the system establish accountability for performance but it also provided a basis for a system of divisional incentives. Thus division management groups were motivated to act to some extent like independent businessmen. They were given considerable freedom to do this, but could be held responsible for, and rewarded according to, their results. Thus the division managers effectively ran their businesses while headquarters appraised their results and established long-term objectives. If the divisions were "well designed," they would be, to a considerable degree, independent of each other; and the burdens of co-ordination among them would be moderate.

The discussion that follows is generally directed toward improving this decentralized form of organization. To do this, the way in which activities are divided into departments, the degree to which decisions are delegated to the departments, and the methods of appraisal and control maintained by the headquarters unit, all must be examined in some detail.

The Prevalence of Decentralization

Following World War II, there was a great deal of discussion among managers and in the business literature of the decentralized or multidivisional form of organization. In the view of some, the trend toward decentralization even became something of a fad, and discussions pro and con based on the experience of particular companies began to appear. This interest led to Chandler's careful study of more than seventy companies that supports a number of useful generalizations.

The nature of a firm's market may be viewed as an essential determinant of its organizational form. If a firm produces a line of similar products using a highly integrated production process and distributing through common channels to a relatively small number of similar customers, it is likely to have a highly centralized, functionally departmentalized type of structure. On the other hand, if the firm has diversified into a variety of markedly different products that are marketed through differing channels to a dissimilar group of customers, the decentralized, multidivisional structure is likely to appear. The steel, copper, and aluminum industries are examples of those that have remained centralized, and perhaps even increased the degree of centralization. The electrical, automobile, power machinery, and chemical industries are examples of those in which diversification of products and markets has been associated with the evolution of the decentralized type of organization. More recently, there has begun to be discussion of the effects of technological advances in data-processing systems on the degree of centralization of an organization. Indeed, some profess to see a counter movement toward more highly centralized structures, which is to be explained in terms of the availability of means for rapidly making a great deal of information about a firm's operations available at a central point. The advent of on-line, real-time data-processing systems clearly presents a firm with opportunities for central control that did not previously exist.

Perhaps it is too soon to see trends generated by the emergence of these data-processing systems, but they do raise some highly relevant questions. The possibility of centralized control presented by modern computers does not, of course, settle the question of its desirability. A firm may thus find this a stimulus to review the motives for centralization and those for decentralization and, perhaps, to re-examine its basic organizational philosophy. If, for example, inventories are to be centrally controlled, then division managers can hardly be held responsible for the imperfections of inventory policy. It may thus become necessary to measure their performance exclusive of the effects of inventory policy and to wonder about the motivational impact of the corresponding reduction in their area of responsibility.

The installation of a large data-processing system is perhaps more revolutionary than evolutionary in nature. A careful study of the organization is required in preparation for it. The decision to proceed has implications that tend to be both irreversible and very expensive. Thus here is a point at which the notion of organization design is most relevant and the need for well-developed hypotheses about centralization and decentralization most pressing.

Three Propositions

Out of the available data on the question of centralization and decentralization in organization design, three propositions or hypotheses emerge that serve to motivate the further study of these problems. Briefly stated, these propositions are:

1. The problem of the proper degree of centralization is non-trivial in the sense that neither a very highly centralized nor a very highly

decentralized form is likely to be most satisfactory. Generally speaking, the good organizational designs lie somewhere between the two extremes.

2. In the majority of cases organizational change might better be described as evolutionary rather than revolutionary. That is, if one takes the long view, the changes in an organization appear more as small, gradual modifications than as sudden, dramatic alterations. The exceptions, of course, would be those changes arising out of some crisis in the organization's life; but even in these cases, a good deal of inertia may be present.

3. The evolutionary process of changing organizational structures is in some cases seriously imperfect in that it contains an element of unstable oscillation between excessive centralization and excessive decentralization. The process of organizational learning seems inadequate for a stable evolutionary development, and instead, a sort of vacillation or "hunting" takes place.

It is the implications of these propositions that suggest the role of the organizational designer and his problems. Each of them is briefly introduced below.

Non-triviality

In the political sphere there is perhaps some agreement that neither complete centralization in the form of dictatorship nor complete decentralization in the form of anarchy can long survive as viable organizational forms. Similarly, economic systems that rely to a high degree on central planning as well as those that are characterized by a high degree of laissez faire tend to evolve toward more moderate forms.[6] In industrial organizations as well, the American experience seems to support the notion that neither extreme is best, and for many firms the "best" organizational form seems to be somewhere between a fully centralized design and a fully decentralized one. If this turns out to be true in an interesting number of cases, the design problem is not as simple as pushing the organization toward one extreme or the other. Rather, the problem becomes one of seeking the right *degree* of centralization or decentralization, a considerably more difficult task. Indeed, if it were to be otherwise, we would probably have long since ceased to wonder about organizational forms in many spheres of activity.

An Evolutionary Process

The proposition that organizational change is most often an evolutionary process is somewhat tautological, depending on the distinction one chooses to make between evolution and revolution. In this context, however, it implies several things:

1. We are speaking of large, complex, social organizations made up of people who tend to resist changes in their organization's form. Such a system cannot be radically changed in the short run and continue to function effectively.

2. Most organizational changes are small ones (in comparison with the complexity of the entire system) and are made in an experimental spirit. That is, the best kind of organizational changes are those that can be made and tested on a small inexpensive scale with some opportunity of recovery if the experiment fails. This may well be viewed as the rational or "optimal" method of organizational change when we must act in the face of very limited knowledge of the consequences of proposed changes.

3. The opportunities to completely design or redesign an organization are relatively rare. Even when a large new organization must be brought into being, one may expect that it will be closely patterned after some existing organization and that its birth will be followed by an extended period of evolution before it functions effectively. Indeed, much of what we do in industry, the military, and the government is aimed at the avoidance of having to bring radically new or redesigned organizations into being. We simply do not presently have the knowledge to do this effectively.

Hunting

The evolution of decentralized organizations sometimes appears to be a relatively efficient process, responding to changes in the firm's environment by adapting organizational structure through relatively few unsuccessful experiments. In marked contrast to this is the phenomenon of "hunting," in which an organization oscillates from one organizational form to another, failing to achieve any long-run equilibrium. In the successful evolutionary process the predominant effects are the responses of the organization to the changes in its environment, say, in terms of markets or technology. Chandler's general hypothesis is that changing environments require changes in corporate strategy, which in turn leads to changes in organizational structure. Hunting, on the other hand, can apparently occur even in the face of generally stable environmental conditions. When the organization finds itself in difficulty, it looks to changes in organizational structure to alleviate the problems. To see how this may result in hunting, it may be useful to consider the following hypothetical process. We imagine a firm operating with a highly centralized organization structure. Management in the central office is concerned in detail with the ongoing operations of all segments of the firm. To deal with these problems, a mass of detailed information is necessary. As the volume of this information grows, it begins to challenge the capacity of the management group. Decisions must be made requiring a detailed knowledge that central management cannot hope to achieve and maintain. The more they delve into the operating problems of one aspect of the firm, the more they must neglect the full sweep of long- and short-range decisions that require their attention. The firm becomes slow in recognizing problems and responding to them. Those at the operating level cannot be held responsible for the results that depend upon central management decisions. Operating managers become frustrated and perhaps seek ways of getting quicker decisions to their own advantage by deliberate deception of top management. When an operating decision is made at the top, it may not be fully effective since it is difficult to communicate the uncertainties and judgments that require intimate experience on the scene. No group in the firm is sufficiently free from the daily pressures of ongoing affairs to concentrate on long-range planning.

Although a high degree of centralization may make for good co-ordination of the over-all actions of the firm and decisions that are more nearly optimal for the firm as a whole, the top managers who are involved soon find themselves unable to handle the volume of work required. Being in a position to appreciate the difficulties brought about by centralization, and in a position to alter the structure of the firm, central management begins to consider the appealing advantages of decentralization. This "grass is always greener" effect leads them to move strongly toward a highly decentralized structure.

If the degree of decentralization achieved is significant, the disadvantages of this type of structure begin to make themselves felt. The activities of subunits tend to become unco-ordinated and conflicting, and perhaps a few glaring incidents show the organization in its worst light. Facilities are duplicated, resources are used wastefully by one unit that are desperately needed by another, and the subunits begin to compete with one another, both in procurement and in marketing. One unit may buy outside the firm at a high price what another unit produces within the firm at a lower price. A few such incidents of lack of co-ordination cry out for the co-ordinative power of central authority, and the organization structure is impelled in this direction. Management, failing to fully recall the difficulties of its previously centralized structure, moves too far back in that direction, and the cycle is ready to repeat itself.

The process by which such an organization learns from experience about itself is clearly deficient. Thus an exaggerated estimate of the disadvantages of the current organizational form coupled with a similarly exaggerated view of the benefits of the alternative form lead the firm into an unstable hunting for non-existent perfection.

The phenomenon of hunting is, of course, somewhat difficult to demonstrate in actuality. Devons found it in his study of wartime planning agencies in Great Britain.[7] It is not surprising to find it in such situations because these organizations had to be formed quickly, often with inexperienced people, and operated in a continual atmosphere of high uncertainty and crisis. This permitted very little of an organization's energies to be devoted to organizational learning and did not encourage stable evolution of structure. One may also see hunting in the history of Soviet Russia since the revolution.[8] Major failures in industry or agriculture seem often to be met with the remedy "more centralization" or "more decentralization," depending on the current state of the system. In industry, for example, the scope of decision permitted the plant manager appears to fluctuate in this way. At the present time a return to such devices as an interest charge on invested capital and a free market in consumer goods are being seriously considered because they permit greater decentralization of production decisions. This is in part the result of some glaring errors on the part of the central planning agencies. One may detect hunting also in the history of some of our own military organizations and in the literature of current business experience. Indeed, a major dimension of any "corporate reorganization" is likely to be a change in the degree of centralization or decentralization, and the cycles may at times become rather frequent.[9]

It is less important to demonstrate hunting as it has occurred than it is to recognize it as a useful hypothesis the organizational designer might consider central to his work. Indeed, it may well be that the major contribution to be made by carefully considered organizational changes is the avoidance of repeatedly unsuccessful experiments that yield nothing in the way of accumulated organizational experience. It is necessary to take the long view. Any structure will have its moments of inadequacy. Centralization may be at its best in times of crisis, but decentralization preferable at other times. Rather than increasing internal confusion and uncertainty through hunting, one might better seek a structure that will have some sort of long-run optimality. Further, the knowledge that each organizational structure has its own advantages and difficulties must be made explicit, and a balanced conception of these must be sought. The need to base decisions on an intimate knowledge of local details will always conflict with the need to co-ordinate decisions for the firm as a whole. The key to organizational design may be finding a way of effectively dividing up these tasks.

We now turn to the problems of saying somewhat more explicitly what it is we wish to study, what is known about it already, and our objectives in the work of organization design.

The Phenomenon under Study

We view organizations as being composed of subdivisions or subunits and permit this view to be applied at various levels of observation.

For example:

Organization	Subunit
A large corporation	An operating division
An operating division	A plant
A plant	A department
A department	A work center

If a subunit

1. does not compete with other subunits for the use of resources such as capital, research services, staff assistance, or management skill, available in limited amounts within the organization

2. does not compete in the same market nor buy from the same sources as other subdivisions

3. does not provide goods or services to other subunits nor depend upon them for its own inputs

4. can make decisions and act without co-ordination with other subunits

5. serves its own objectives without considering the objectives of the other subunits or of the organization

—then we would say that the subunit is highly self-contained. If these things are true of all of the subunits that compose the organization, we would regard the organization as a highly decentralized one. To the degree that these statements fail to describe the subunits of an organization, we would regard it as less decentralized, or more centralized.

We shall attempt to investigate a range of problems in the design and management of organizations that involves as a major consideration the degree to which an organization is centralized or decentralized. Our concern will be with the pattern of assignment of organizational functions to subunits and with the arrangement of information flows and decision-making responsibilities associated with these patterns. The discussion will focus on the relations between a profile of measures of organizational performance and such organizational characteristics as:

Self-containment or interdependence of subunits

Pattern of delegation of decisions

Pattern of information flows

Amount of co-ordination among subunits

Perhaps the best way to make some of these ideas clear is to examine a simple, specific problem in which some of these issues arise.

An Illustrative Problem: The Elevator System

A bank of elevators serves a tall building. The state of the system at any time might be described by the following dimensions:

> The number and destinations of people waiting at each floor for transportation

> The predicted rate at which people will demand transportation between each pair of floors as a function of time

> The location of each elevator and its direction of movement

> The number and destinations of people on each elevator

System parameters include:

> Number of elevators

> Number of floors

> Travel times

> Loading and unloading times

The objective of the system is to minimize the average time a person spends between indicating his need for transportation and delivery at his destination.

One might consider two decision structures:

> *Decentralized.*—Each elevator is controlled by an operator who moves at his own discretion.

> *Centralized.*—Each elevator is controlled by an operator who moves according to instructions given by a dispatcher located at the bottom floor.

For each decision structure one might consider a variety of associated information structures. For example, under the decentralized decision structure an operator might know only:

> The location and direction of movement of his own car

> The number of people in his car destined for each floor

> For each floor, whether or not there was a demand for service, but not the numbers or destinations of the people involved

One might be interested in such questions as:

> What would be the result of various patterns of decision-making behavior on the part of the operators?

What, if any, improvement in performance could be expected if more information about the state of the system were made available to each operator?

Similarly, under centralized management, the dispatcher might be provided with varying information structures. For each, one might ask about the relative effectiveness of various policies, the advantages of providing additional information, and how the results compare with those from various decentralized information-decision structures. (Note that under centralization the dispatcher's orders constitute information that an operator may or may not know at any given time.)

This system thus illustrates such concepts as:

An organization and its subunits

Alternate patterns of delegation of decisions

Patterns of information flow

Co-ordination among subunits

Self-containment or interdependence of subunits

What Is Known

There is a relatively modest amount of literature dealing directly with centralization and decentralization of industrial organizations. On the other hand, the problem has such broad implications that there is a large amount of literature that is potentially relevant. The bibliography at the close of this discussion represents an attempt to survey the literature dealing more or less directly with the problem. Several types of work appear in this literature.

There are empirical studies that present data and interpretations on the growth and structure of industrial organizations. Of these the most directly relevant is that of Chandler, on which we have drawn extensively. There are studies that present data on specific aspects of management and organizations—such as the studies of the capital-budgeting function—that are useful in the discussion that follows.[10] There is a good deal of reporting in the business literature of what is going on in particular firms and industries.[11] Although these are hardly objective data, they are most useful in sensitizing one to the problems the managers find of current concern.

There is a considerable volume of economic theory relating to central planning and decentralization of economic decisions through the price system.[12] Some of it is relevant in the sense that is suggests ideas that might be adopted at the organizational level. The proposal, for example, that the central planning agency announce prices and then observe the response of producers and consumers to these prices is a direct parallel of certain transfer-price systems in industry. In the economic case, the central planner notes the action of profit-maximizing participants and then readjusts prices until production and consumption are in balance. In the industrial case, central management announces the price at which goods will be transferred from a producing division to a consuming division. Both divisions are supposed to act so as to maximize their divisional profit, and central management uses the transfer price as a means of co-ordinating the production of one with the consumption of the other. It is not necessary for top management to be concerned with the operating details of either division but only to observe their responses to various transfer prices. Considerable development in the context of linear programming has gone on that attempts to show an organization designer how such transfer prices (or accounting prices) might be fixed in order to achieve profit maximization for the firm as a whole.[13]

There are also a number of studies that begin (as this one does) the formulation of models that might be useful to the designer in dealing with the question of centralization and decentralization.[14] This work must move toward greater realism at the designer's level of observation, greater attention to the details of organizational processes, and consideration of a wider range of relevant variables if it is to be made more useful. This is in part the motivation for what follows.

Perhaps more useful than any attempt to summarize the diverse literature in these areas would be a rough statement of some of the hypotheses it suggests. These may serve to raise some interesting and fruitful questions about centralization and decentralization. Although we may not be able to give answers to these questions, asking them may be the most useful approach to the problem of organization design in the present state of knowledge. Nothing is asserted about the confirmation of these hypotheses. They are simply intended to suggest the sort of questions that have been raised and appear interesting. They indicate the need for fundamental theory that will permit them to be interrelated, and the need for making many of the concepts involved operationally meaningful.

Some General Hypotheses

1. The tendency to decentralize is related to the size of the organization.

   a) The tendency to decentralize will be stronger in those organizations where diseconomies of scale operate in production than in those organizations in which economies of scale are present.

   b) The tendency to decentralize will be stronger in those organizations in which diseconomies of scale operate in management than in those where economies of scale are present.

c) Geographical decentralization is seldom followed by decentralization of communication and control.

d) Decentralization of communication and control is often followed by geographical decentralization.

e) The tendency to decentralize is related to the number of differentiated functions in an organization, which in turn is related to the size and age of the organization.

f) The fewer the number of operational linkages between the components of an organization, the greater the tendency to decentralize.

2. The greater the urgency of a decision and the shorter the time in which to make it, the greater the tendency to centralize.

a) Crisis favors intuition over analysis.

b) Crisis reduces the number of alternatives considered.

c) Crisis reduces the amount of communication within the organization, but increases the amount of control.

d) Crisis can be dealt with faster under decentralized communication and control than under centralized.

e) The amount of information brought to bear upon a crisis is greater under decentralization.

3. The greater the potential consequences of a decision, the more likely it is to be centralized.

4. Given an organizational goal, component subgoals can be postulated that will be consistent with the organizational goal and with decentralization of communication and control.

5. Centralization may lead to "better" decisions; however, the savings in communication through decentralization more than offset any decline in the "goodness" of decisions.

6. Given the limited human and organizational capacities for data-handling, computation, and decision, decentralization will be more effective than centralization.

7. A decision-maker is more strongly motivated to serve a component subgoal than he is to serve an organizational goal.

8. Decentralized organizations can be designed that place less strain on the data-handling, computation, and decision-making capabilities of the participants, and yet produce "satisfactory" attainment of organizational goals.

9. The faster, cheaper, and more noise-free the communication system, the less the tendency to decentralize.

10. Decentralization increases the tendency to duplicate differentiated staff services.

11. Component managers in a decentralized organization tend to favor short-run attainment of component subgoals against long-run attainment, if such attainment is related to upward or horizontal mobility in the organization.

12. Component managers are faced with a class of decisions for which they have more information and are more effective in using it than centralized-system managers.

13. The effectiveness of decentralization is directly related to the degree to which component outputs can be measured.

14. The fewer the operational linkages between components, the more effective will be a decentralized organization design.

15. New ideas and techniques will be made operational more quickly in a decentralized organization.

16. In general, the most effective organizational design will fall somewhere between complete centralization and complete decentralization.

17. The greater the degree of decentralization, the less reliance placed on the advice of staff specialists.

18. The higher the skill level of the manager, the greater the tendency to decentralize.

19. The greater the degree of decentralization, the broader the statements of policy used throughout the organization.

20. In general, no organization is likely to produce optimal decisions, but decentralized organizations can produce decisions that achieve the same levels of satisfaction as those produced by centralized organizations.

21. Decentralization of shared resources does not decrease their utilization.

22. Decentralization of shared resources increases the level of service rendered.

23. The costs (in a most general sense) of co-ordination and communication increase non-linearly with the size of the management hierarchy of an organization.

24. Centralization decreases the tendency to measure the effectiveness of organizational components.

25. Decentralized decision-makers tend to view their roles as being characterized by a greater degree of self-determination and independence.

26. Decentralized decision-makers tend to view their roles as more directly serving their own self-interest at the same time as serving the component subgoals.

27. Decentralization provides a means of having in certain respects the advantages of bigness and smallness at the same time.

28. The smaller the organization, the greater the influence of individual personalities.

29. The greater the flexibility of an organization in shifting between centralized and decentralized patterns of operation, the more effective its performance.

30. The basic motivational effect of decentralization is that of bringing the reward closer to the effort.

31. Each subunit decision that is dependent on the decisions of other subunits must either

   a) Have its consequences reflected in the criterion function of the subunit, or,

   b) Be subject to co-ordination

32. The greater the degree of decentralization, the greater the tendency of headquarters management to reduce organizational slack by overstressing the subunits.

33. A side effect of decentralization is the training of a larger number of experienced decision-makers.

34. A fundamental goal in the design of a decentralized organization is to match the demands of the organization to the information-handling and decision-making capacities of the executives.

35. Subunits tend to evolve so as to match and utilize the skills of particular managers, despite management's efforts to prevent it.

36. The headquarters group is to some extent a captive of the subunits because it must depend upon them for information.

37. A fundamental principle in the design of decentralized organizations is to place the long-term strategic decisions in the hands of the headquarters group but to leave the tactical or operating decisions in the hands of the operating units.

38. The greater the degree of centralization, the greater the ratio of indirect to direct costs.

39. Operating subunits tend to build specialized staff groups that duplicate those provided by the headquarters group.

40. There exist some items of overhead that cost no more to provide for several subunits than for one.

41. The greater the uncertainty associated with a decision, the greater the tendency for it to be delegated.

42. The greater the uncertainty, the greater the tendency for subunits to absorb or suppress it.

43. The greater the uncertainty associated with a decision, the more costly it becomes to transmit information about the decision.

Organization Design: Objectives and Strategy

It would be naïve to suppose that anyone in the near future could, based on well-supported knowledge, design a large industrial organization in any great detail. The concept of organization design that is realistic at present is not that of the machine designer. The underlying fund of knowledge about organizational phenomena is far too limited. Nonetheless, we are moving toward the consideration of larger and larger problems in the field of organization planning, and already it has become important, for example, to plan information-flow systems for rather substantial organizations. Knowledge about organizations is beginning to be brought together in forms potentially useful to the designer, and we are learning what questions need to be asked about organizations.

The concept of organization design relevant here is a more limited one, but it is not without significance. We may think of the designer's role as essentially that of speeding up and making more efficient the evolutionary processes by which organizations grow and change. The process of evolution is viewed as a series of experiments, no one of which brings radical changes in the organization but which collectively produce organizational transformations. The important contribution of the designer can be:

1. To suggest what experiments can best be done based on some carefully developed hypotheses

2. To help the organization obtain the most information from the experiments that are done

3. To reduce so far as possible the number of these experiments that fail to produce satisfactory results

4. To prevent the phenomenon of hunting by designing effective systems for organizational learning

The equipment the designer needs for such tasks includes well-developed hypotheses that suggest experiments and sensitize him to results, and the techniques for conducting and analyzing such experiments. The work of this discussion may be viewed as that of contributing to the designer's arsenal of hypotheses.[15]

Basic Problems

Broadly speaking, there are two basic problems in organization design. The first of these is the problem of how to divide the activities of the firm among the subunits in an effective way. Activities are grouped in such a way as to take advantage of certain complementarities (the name we have given to the existence of an interdependency between two activities that makes it less costly to undertake them together rather than separately) that exist among them and to minimize the amount of co-ordination required among the resulting subunits. Of course, the activities considered include decision-making activities. This is a difficult problem to take beyond the level of the obvious and resists solution by logical methods of allocation.[16]

The second problem is that of finding effective methods of producing co-ordination among the subunits of a firm. Here, two general attacks may be seen. On the one hand, we may be concerned with developing better information-flow systems for the firm so that co-ordination may be made more effective. On the other hand, we may try to develop methods for actually reducing the amount of information flow necessary to produce co-ordination. It is in this latter area that many of the most interesting problems associated with decentralization appear to fall. Suppose, for example, one could instruct a division manager to operate much as an independent businessman, maximizing some measure of divisional profit; and suppose further that if each division manager did this, the result would be to maximize profit for the firm as a whole. If such a system could be designed, it would reduce to a minimum the amount of co-ordination necessary among the divisions. Although such a system may never be realized, interesting efforts are being made at such reductions in co-ordinative effort. In the next chapter some basic concepts are suggested that may assist in the exploration of these problems.

1. See Alfred D. Chandler, Jr., *Strategy and Structure* (Cambridge, Mass.: M.I.T. Press, 1962) and Alfred P. Sloan, Jr., *My Years with General Motors* (Garden City, N.Y.: Doubleday & Co., 1964).

2. Useful references on organizational growth and size include: E. P. Adler, "Relationships between Organization Size and Efficiency," *Management Science,* VII,

No. 1 (1960); Reinhard Bendix, *Work and Authority in Industry* (New York: John Wiley & Sons, 1956), pp. 211–26; Kenneth Boulding, "The Jungle of Hugeness," *Saturday Review,* May 17, 1958; Sune Carlson, *Executive Behavior* (Stockholm: C. A. Stromberg, 1959); Sidney Hook, "Bureaucrats Are Human," *Saturday Review,* May 17, 1958; James G. March and Herbert A. Simon, *Organizations* (New York: John Wiley & Sons, 1958), chap. 2; E. T. Penrose, *The Theory of the Growth of the Firm* (Oxford, Eng.: Blackwells, 1959); N. S. Ross, "Management and the Size of the Firm," *Review of Economic Studies,* XIX (1951); Francis W. Terrien and Donald L. Mills, "The Effect of Changing Size upon the Internal Structure of Organization," *American Sociological Review,* XX, No. 1 (1951).

3. Mason Haire, "Biological Models and Empirical Histories of the Growth of Organizations," in *Modern Organization Theory,* ed. Mason Haire (New York: John Wiley & Sons, 1959).

4. A. W. Baker and R. C. Davis, *Ratios of Staff to Line Employees and Stages of Differentiation of Staff Functions* (Columbus, Ohio: Ohio State University Bureau of Business Research, 1954).

5. Chandler, *op. cit.,* pp. 299–314.

6. The current indications of economic difficulties in Soviet Russia provide a good example. These difficulties are being met by an increasing reliance on "decentralizing" devices such as a free market for consumer goods, interest charges on capital invested in plant and equipment, and profit measures for industrial plants.

7. Ely Devons, *Planning in Practice* (Cambridge, Eng.: Cambridge University Press, 1950).

8. See for example Georg von Rauch, *A History of Soviet Russia* (New York: F. A. Praeger, 1957).

9. Reports of this sort appear from time to time in *Business Week, Forbes,* and similar journals.

10. The relevant references may be found in Chapter III.

11. See, for example, *Business Week, Forbes, Fortune, Wall Street Journal,* etc.

12. A good example is Benjamin E. Lippincott (ed.), *On the Economic Theory of Socialism* (Minneapolis: University of Minnesota Press, 1938).

13. See Chapter IX.

14. For example, Robert Dorfman, Paul Samuelson, and Robert Solow, *Linear Programming and Economic Analysis* (New York: McGraw-Hill, 1958); Thomas Marschak, "Centralization and Decentralization in Economic Organization," *Econometrics,* XXVII, No. 3 (July, 1959), 399–430; and Martin Shubik, "Incentives, Decentralized Control, the Assignment of Joint Costs and Internal Pricing," *Management Science,* VIII, No. 3 (April, 1962), 325–43.

15. The importance of well-developed hypotheses in this context is discussed in William T. Morris, *Management Science in Action* (Homewood, Ill.: Richard D. Irwin, 1963), pp. 125–41.

16. James G. March and Herbert A. Simon, *Organizations* (New York: John Wiley & Sons, 1958), pp. 22–33.

CHAPTER 2

COMPLEMENTARITY AND CO-ORDINATION

Basic Concepts

An organization is primarily a device for overcoming the limited capacities of individual persons to process information and make decisions. Yet these limitations remain the most constraining factor in the evolution and design of the organization. As soon as the work of the organization grows beyond the capacities of one man, the two basic problems of organizational design immediately emerge. These are the problems of how to divide the work of the organization among its members and of how to co-ordinate the activities of the members. The fundamental problem is that of finding an organizational form that combines a "good" division of work with a reasonable burden of co-ordination effort. The fact that forms satisfactory from one of these viewpoints are often unsatisfactory from the other lies at the base of many design difficulties.

In a large organization that carries on many different kinds of activities, this basic limitation of human capacity works against a high degree of centralization of decision-making. The more centralized the control, the more general become the bases upon which decisions are made and the fewer the details and relationships that can be taken into account. It becomes necessary thus to find a way of dividing up the work of the organization into relatively self-contained tasks to be carried on by administrative subunits, and then to find ways of co-ordinating the work of the subunits toward the objectives of the organization as a whole.

In order to give some structure to the complexities of organizational design, it may be useful to think in terms of these two basic questions:

1. How should the activities of the organization be broken down for assignment to subunits?

2. How can co-ordination among the resulting subunits be assured?

Though it is difficult to say very precisely what is meant by a subunit, it has roughly the following characteristics:

1. There is a person or small group of persons responsible for seeing that the subunit carries on a reasonably well-defined set of activities. This responsibility includes that of co-ordinating the activities within the subunit.

2. Typically, the subunit has within itself most of the resources necessary to carry out its activities. Thus there is more co-ordination taking place within the subunit than there is among subunits. In other words, efforts are made toward establishing relatively self-contained or independent subunits.

These characteristics, like many of the concepts that follow, are somewhat difficult to discuss in general terms because they are matters of degree and because the meaning of the terms tends to change as one examines various levels of an organization.

The question of how large a subunit should be has traditionally been discussed in terms of the notion of span of control. This essentially measures the number of subordinates supervised by a superior. Span of control has not turned out to be a very useful concept because simply counting subordinates does not provide a sufficiently precise measure to yield any very fruitful general principles. Although the scale of activities as measured by the number of persons supervised may be a first approximation, it does not generally reflect the information-handling or decision-making load placed on a supervisor. Indeed, as Chandler has shown, subunits can become quite large if the activities they perform have a considerable degree of uniformity.[1] When, however, activities become diverse, subunits must be made smaller. By grouping activities into larger subunits, one may obtain better co-ordination among them; but this is paid for by the greater generality and lesser attention to detail that must characterize the decisions and policies. The point is simply that questions of this sort do not appear to yield to gross measures like span of control. To work effectively, the designer will have to consider the activities and structure of the organization at a more microscopic level. It is in pursuit of this hypothesis that the following analysis is directed. Our general objective is to find designs that will simultaneously bring to the firm both the advantages of bigness and smallness without an undue burden from the disadvantages of either.

Forming Subunits

The formation of subunits or the dividing up of the tasks in an organization often appears to be based on some relatively simple concept. For example, considering a firm as a whole, one may find subunits that appear to be based on such principles as:

1. Activities that contribute to the production of a given product, line of products, or service

2. Activities that serve a particular market or group of customers

3. Activities that involve particular skills, professional qualifications, processes, or functions

4. Activities that are carried on in a particular geographical region

5. Activities that are to be completed in a particular time period, such as long-range and short-range planning

At the level of a plant we often find departmentalization based on either similar processes and functions or on product. At the level of the individual, activities may be assigned either on the basis of skill or on the basis of product.

The data presently available tend to support some generalizations involving these concepts. For example, as an organization grows, it tends often to departmentalize at first on a process or functional basis. If it continues to grow, and especially if this is associated with a diversification of products and activities, process departmentalization tends to give way to product departmentalization. Within the resulting product departments, however, process subunits reappear. This sort of effect can be explained in terms of the advantages of various task groupings or complementarities and the associated co-ordination effort required. As long as the firm produces a product or line of products that is sold to a small number of customers or to a relatively uniform group of customers, complementarities dominate the organizational form and lead to functional designs with units for purchasing, production, sales, accounting, engineering, and so on. The major task of co-ordination arises through the need to respond to changing market conditions. As long as the firm faces a single market, the costs (both in time and money) of co-ordinating the functional departments are not great.

Indeed, co-ordination can become rather routinized; and even if the firm grows large, the burden of co-ordination among the functional departments does not increase proportionately.

However, when the firm diversifies into new lines and begins to serve quite different markets with quite different products, two effects become significant. This diversification brings an increase in the size of the firm and thus an increase in the level of activities in the functional departments. However, the marginal advantages accruing from grouping activities in these functional departments begin to decrease. The burden of co-ordination (again, in both cost and time) among the functional departments seriously increases.

The firm's response to this may be to rearrange the activities so as to produce product-oriented organizational units that are to a considerable degree self-contained and thus reduce the burdens of co-ordination. At the same time, activities within these units are grouped into subunits to take advantage of complementarities. Hopefully, the level of activities in these subunits is sufficiently great so that net decline in the benefits of complementarities is less than the increased savings through reductions in co-ordination requirements. The firm may not go all the way in disbanding the functional departments. In some cases the burdens of co-ordination do not outweigh the advantages of complementarity, and a headquarters division emerges that contains certain functional units to serve the other divisions. Coupled with this response may be the development of devices to further reduce co-ordination requirements among organizational units. The point is that although it may be a necessary condition, size alone does not produce this alteration in organizational form. It is largely the result of complexity arising from diversification.

Departmentalization

In forming a set of activities for assignment to an organizational unit, there are several predominant considerations.

1. The activities should be grouped together to take maximum advantage of complementarities among them. A complementarity exists when it is more profitable to perform a group of activities together in the same unit than it is to perform them separately in different units. A major task of the designer is to identify these complementarities and evaluate them.

2. The activities assigned to a particular subunit should be reasonably capable of co-ordination by a single responsible manager.

3. The activities assigned to a given subunit should be independent so far as possible of the activities carried on by other subunits.

4. The subunit should have a reasonably well-defined objective or output, and should contain within itself, so far as possible, the resources and abilities for its achievement. In this way the output can be measured, and the manager held accountable for the performance of his unit.

5. Those activities that require the greatest amount of co-ordination should be grouped together. This is based on the presumption that co-ordination among activities within the subunit is less expensive and more effective than co-ordination among subunits. If co-ordination costs can be reduced by bringing activities together, this reduction may itself be considered one of the results of complementarity among the activities.

6. Activities whose performance is hindered by grouping them together should be placed in different subunits. These effects might be called reverse complementarities. The most important example is probably that of giving the same unit responsibility for both long-range planning and day-to-day operating problems. The pressure of current problems tends to preclude the performance of long-range planning. Indeed, the basic element of the decentralized structure is the separation of these activities.

7. In so far as possible, each unit should contain the capacity to initiate improvements in its operations, but ideally this innovation should not lead the unit away from accomplishment of the organization's objectives.

Thus it would appear that the two basic concepts in the formation of organizational subunits are the concepts of complementarity and co-ordination. These we next examine in some detail.

Complementarities

Organizational units evolve, or are designed to bring together, activities that can be accomplished more effectively in terms of time, cost, or revenue when done together than when done in distinct self-contained organizational units. A basic task in grouping activities is to identify and evaluate these effects, which may be variously called complementarities, non-additivities, super-additivities, or economies of scale. Complementarity among activities arises basically out of the possibility of having the activities share some resource required for their execution. Sharing here simply implies that the cost of some resource increases less than proportionately when activities are combined in some way, thus producing a reduction in the average cost per unit of activity. This phenomenon appears, however, in some seemingly quite different forms; for example:

1. Set-up costs or fixed costs of all sorts.

2. As the volume of activity increases, more specialized equipment or people may be used, bringing about higher fixed costs due to set-up in the most general sense, but lower marginal cost.

3. Effects resulting from the operation of random phenomena, these being, generally, variance reduction effects. These effects produce opportunities for various activities to share in the *protection,* or to benefit from the function, of insurance funds, reserve machines, emergency equipment, inventories, and so on. The sharing is possible because of the random way in which demands arise.

Complementarities may be sometimes understood in terms of the notion of indivisibility. That is, machines, plants, and people tend to be available in indivisible units of productive capacity. If, in order to carry out some activity, we must buy a machine or hire a research chemist, and the activity in question does not fully utilize the machine or man, then other activities may be added. Because of this indivisibility, the cost per unit of output goes down as we approach the capacity of the man or machine. Thus one may find it desirable to have one computer at company headquarters rather than one in each divisional office, or perhaps a single chemical research group rather than several for the firm.

When a firm grows, either by increasing the volume of production in its present line of products or by diversifying into new product lines, it is likely to be taking advantage of some indivisibility or some unused productive resource. Having obtained a more or less indivisible "bundle" in the form of a skilled management group, a research laboratory, or a production facility, the firm, finding that the bundle is not fully utilized, looks around for other activities. If the firm's unused resources are in the area of management skills and experience, it may take on new activities, perhaps in the form of entire companies. In the resulting organization, decision-making will tend to be centralized in order to take advantage of the available management abilities.

The essence of complementarity is a non-linear or non-additive relation between activities. It is just such relations that are most difficult to deal with intuitively and thus benefit from analysis most often. A very simple example of non-additive effects may serve to establish this point most effectively. The famous economic lot-size problem has many versions and degrees of complication, but its essence is this. There is a production process with an output rate considerably in excess of the rate at which its product is required for use. Thus instead of running the process continuously, it is used intermittently for the product in question. At other times it may be used for the production of different products. The basic question of operating policy is how often to make a run of the product and how much to produce each time a run is made. In attacking this problem it is usually assumed that a planning period of length T is used, and that the amount of product required at a uniform rate over this period is known to be D units. If the lot size is given by L, then

$$\frac{D}{L} = \text{number of lots required during } T.$$

The costs that depend on the choice of L are taken to be of two kinds: those that depend on the lot size (variable costs) and those that are independent of the lot size (fixed costs). Set-up costs are usually assumed to be independent of the lot size, and are defined to include all costs of getting the production of a lot under way and terminating it when completed. Storage costs are computed on the basis of the average amount of product in storage.

Assume that the following costs are given:

C_1 = set-up cost per lot

C_2 = storage cost per piece per unit time, based on average number
of units in storage

Let

$C(L)$ = set-up cost and storage cost for a planning period T, using a
lot size of L

The cost $C(L)$ may be computed as follows:

$$C(L) = C_1 \frac{D}{L} + C_2 \frac{LT}{2}.$$

It is easily verified that if one sets the first derivative of $C(L)$ with respect to L equal to zero, and solves for L, the result is

$$L_0 = \sqrt{\frac{2C_1 D}{C_2 T}}.$$

This is the lot size that minimizes the sum of set-up costs and storage costs. Using this lot size, the total cost per planning period is

$$C(L_0) = \sqrt{2C_1 C_2 DT}$$

and the average cost per unit produced is

$$AC(L_0) = \sqrt{\frac{2C_1 C_2 T}{D}}.$$

Suppose now we can arrange to operate this production facility as a centralized producer for a number of divisions of a firm, each of which has a requirement for the product in question. What will be the benefit of such a grouping of activities? The above relations suggest that grouping activities and thus increasing the demand D will increase the total cost only in proportion to the square root of D. The average cost per unit produced will decline in a manner inversely proportional to the square root of demand. These relations may not be entirely clear on the basis of intuition alone, and thus the analysis may be useful to the designer in deciding whether the benefits from establishing a centralized production facility will outweigh whatever costs arise as a result of doing so. Note that the above remarks apply only to set-up and storage costs.

Complementarities Depending on Random Phenomena

There are a large number of more or less obvious conditions and effects that lead to potential complementarities of interest to the designer. One thinks immediately of set-up and changeover costs in production, high volume buying, special knowledge and ability, by-products, selling the "full line," and so on. In addition there is a whole range of "overhead items" such as accounting, advertising, research, long-range planning, quality control, and the like, that may involve costs that are less than proportional to the volume of output they serve. Somewhat subtler, but equally important, are certain complementarities whose effects can be understood by viewing them as essentially random phenomena. We turn now to some examples of these.

It has long been known that when a resource must be provided in advance in anticipation of a varying demand, important savings can be realized by establishing a "common pool" of the resource to serve an aggregation of such demands. Thus, for example, a distributor who wishes to hold a reserve inventory of some commodity in anticipation of varying demands from retail outlets finds that as the number of retail outlets is increased, the size of the inventory need not be increased proportionally. Thus he can furnish equal "protection" or "insurance" to a larger number of stores at a smaller cost per store or per unit sold. This complementarity, which is achieved by aggregating demands, is the basis for all "insurance" activities, such as the provision of spare machines or people. It permits large firms to realize savings in the face of variable demands for such resources as cash, inventories, plant capacity, manpower, specialized management services, and so on. It helps to explain why there is a tendency to aggregate demands through the centralization of certain activities. Examples include equipment pools, central inventories, secretarial pools, and centralized computer facilities.

To illustrate the basic principles involved and to show how the designer might make a beginning at quantifying these, it may be helpful to examine a specific problem in the planning of an inventory system. The commodity being inventoried may be any resource for which a reserve must be provided in advance of randomly varying demands. It might consist of cash, manpower, goods, plant capacity, or a service capability.

Complementarities in Inventory Systems

To illustrate, suppose that there exists a firm that is organized into operating divisions and a headquarters division. Demands for the commodity in question arise at the operating divisions. The history of the firm is divided into time periods at the beginning of each of which the firm wishes to establish a stock of the commodity, and this stock must suffice for operations during the period. No additional stock may be obtained until the beginning of the subsequent period. For simplicity we shall assume that the firm bases its planning on one such period, rather than looking ahead several periods in the future when formulating policy. The questions facing the firms are:

1. How much inventory should be provided?

2. How much of this inventory should be located at each of the operating divisions, and how much at the headquarters division?

To make these problems explicit, let

d_j = demand for the commodity during a period at operating division j $(j = 1, \cdot \cdot \cdot, N)$

$f(d_j)$ = probability distribution of d_j, having a mean m_j and standard deviation s_j

$$D = \sum_{j=1}^{N} d_j \text{ total demand for the firm during the period}$$

I_j = the inventory provided at division j for a period $(I_h = $ headquarters inventory)

For simplicity as well, suppose that there is a storage cost of c_1 dollars per unit stocked, which is based on the number of units remaining at the end of an inventory period. This cost is the same throughout the firm. There is also a shortage cost proportional to the amount of the commodity that is demanded but cannot be supplied, say, c_2 dollars per unit. Management wishes to adopt policies that minimize expected cost.

Suppose first that the firm considers a fully decentralized design, in which each operating division holds its own inventory and none is held at headquarters. High shipping costs prevent stock at one division from being used to satisfy demands arising at another division. Each division will establish an inventory that will minimize the function

$$C(I_j) = c_1 \int_{d_j=0}^{I_j} (I_j - d_j)f(d_j)dd_j + c_2 \int_{d_j=I_j}^{\infty} (d_j - I_j)f(d_j)dd_j .$$

The result will be to choose an inventory that will satisfy the equation

$$F(I_j) = \frac{c_2}{c_1 + c_2}$$

where

$$F(I_j) = \int_{d_j=0}^{I_j} f(d_j)dd_j .$$

The expected cost of such a policy will generally increase if the standard deviation of the demand distribution, s_j, is increased. If we assume that the demand distribution is normal, the expected cost is directly proportional to its standard deviation. To use this fact, we now assume that the demand at each division is a normally distributed random variable.[2]

Thus if we take I_j to be the expected cost minimizing inventory for division j, the cost at that division is given by

$$C(I_j) = ks_j$$

and the amount of inventory held by each division will be

$$I_j = m_j + as_j .$$

The value of a may be found from a table of the standard normal integral. If $\frac{c_2}{c_1 + c_2} \geq .50$, then $a \geq 0$; otherwise, $a < 0$. For the firm as a whole, this design will result in a total inventory of

$$\sum_j I_j = \sum_j m_j - a \sum_j s_j$$

and a total expected cost of

$$\sum_i C(I_i) = k \sum_i s_i .$$

Suppose now that the firm considers a fully centralized design in which all inventory is to be held at headquarters, thus aggregating the demands from the operating divisions hoping to take advantage of possible complementarities. We neglect at first any additional costs of delays that may result from supplying these demands from a headquarters stock as opposed to divisional stocks. The demand at headquarters is given by D, a normally distributed random variable with mean

$$m_h = \sum_i m_i$$

and variance s_h^2. This value of this variance is the crucial point on which complementarity depends.

If the demands at the divisions are independent, then

$$s_h^2 = \sum_i s_i^2 .$$

In this case the inventory chosen by the headquarters division will be

$$I_h = m_h + a s_h$$

and the cost for the firm will be

$$C(I_h) = k s_h .$$

The critical point is that, assuming independence,

$$s_h < \sum_i s_i$$

and thus the cost for the centralized design will be less than that for the decentralized plan. This reduction in cost is what one would call the saving due to the complementarity among the divisional demands and inventories.

It is interesting to note that if $\dfrac{c_2}{c_1 + c_2} > .50$, then $a > 0$, and the amount of inventory held by the firm in the centralized design will be less than the amount under decentralization. If, however, $\dfrac{c_2}{c_1 + c_2} < .50$, then more inventory will be held under centralization than under decentralization, although complementarities still exist in terms of costs.

The magnitude of the savings due to complementarities may be most easily shown in the case in which the divisional demands have equal standard deviations, $s_j = s$ for all j. The inventory held under the decentralized design $\sum_j I_j$ will differ from the inventory under centralization I_h by the amount

$$\sum_j I_j - I_h = aNs - aN^{1/2}s = aN^{1/2}s(N^{1/2} - 1).$$

Thus as the number of divisions is increased, the difference in the firm's inventories under the two plans would increase. If $a > 0$, the reduction in inventory due to complementarity will increase as the number of divisions is increased. The cost difference between the two designs is given, in this special case by

$$\sum_j C(I_j) - C(I_h) = kNs - kN^{1/2}s = kN^{1/2}s(N^{1/2} - 1).$$

This cost difference is always positive, indicating that the savings due to complementarities increase as the number of divisions increases.

If, instead of being independent, the demands at the divisions are perfectly correlated with each other, the standard deviation of demand under a centralized design behaves differently. Let

$$d_j = a_j + b_j d_1.$$

Then

$$s_h^2 = \left(\sum_j b_j\right) s_1^2.$$

Now if all the b_j are greater than, or equal to, zero (if there is a positive correlation among the divisional demands), there will be no difference in the inventory or costs under the two designs. If, on the other hand, some of the b_j are positive and some are negative, there may be savings due to complementarities. In the extreme case in which $\sum_j b_j = 0$ the variations in demand at some divisions are exactly canceled by variations at other divisions, permitting expected cost under a centralized design to be reduced to zero.

If the demands at the division are neither perfectly independent nor perfectly correlated, the complementarities may be illustrated as follows.

Consider a firm with only two divisions. The demand at headquarters under a centralized design is given by

$$D = d_1 + d_2 .$$

The variance of demand at headquarters is

$$s_h^2 = s_1^2 + s_2^2 + 2r_{12}s_1s_2$$

where r_{12} is the coefficient of correlation between the divisional demands. Thus one could hypothesize that maximum complementarity will occur for $r_{12} = -1$ (perfect negative correlation), and the degree of complementarity will decrease as the correlation between the demands increases. For $r_{12} = 0$ we have the case of independence, and for $r_{12} = 1$ we have perfect positive correlation with complementarity disappearing entirely.

An important assumption has been made that contributes to the tendency of this firm to take advantage of complementarity by centralization. This is the assumption that additional costs or delays due to supplying demands from a headquarters stock may be neglected. Further, it has been assumed that there are to be no "cross-shipments" between divisions; that is, inventory at one division is not used to satisfy demands arising at another division. These assumptions may now be modified to illustrate very simply some conditions under which decentralized designs would be preferred.

If we add a penalty cost that is incurred when demands are met from the headquarters inventory, it is possible that this penalty could negate any advantages due to complementarity. Suppose that for every unit of demand met from the headquarters supply there is a cost for shipping and delay of c_3. Then the cost of a centralized design will be

$$c(I_h) = c_3 \sum_j m_j .$$

If we assume that some complementarity exists, as c_3 increases the least costly design will shift from a centralized one to a decentralized one.

If we consider the cost c_3 above and further make the assumption that cross-shipments are permitted between operating divisions at no cost, the preferred design is a decentralized one. Free cross-shipment permits a decentralized design to take advantage of exactly the same degree of complementarity that could be utilized in a centralized system.

If we assume an equal charge for cross-shipments between any two divisions or between headquarters and any division, we have a system that has been studied by Krishnan and Rao.[3] Their results confirm one's expectation that the preferred system will be a decentralized one. As the cost of cross-shipments is increased, the preferred system will have inventories and expected costs that approach those of the previously discussed decentralized system with no cross-shipments permitted. The lower the cost of cross-shipment, the smaller the total amount of inventory held by the firm. As long as some cross-shipment does occur, one may predict that if the divisions have equal standard deviations of demand, the inventory per division will decrease as the number of divisions increases.

In considering these systems, it is wise to keep in mind the sort of communication or co-ordination problems they imply. In a fully centralized system, for example, the headquarters division must have information on demand from all the divisions in order to formulate policy for the firm. Presumably, this information must be revised from time to time. The divisions, on the other hand, cannot know whether a particular demand will be satisfied until they have been informed about the situation by headquarters. In a fully decentralized system with no cross-shipments, complete self-containment has been achieved, and the divisions may proceed with their own formulations of inventory policy without reference to the activities of other divisions or of the headquarters group. In a fully decentralized system with cross-shipment taking place, no division can fix its own inventory policy without knowledge of what is being done at all other divisions. Any division is in the position of having part of its inventory potentially supplied by the other divisions, and similarly it acts in part as an inventory holder for the other divisions. Indeed, inventories cannot be fixed optimally in this case without essentially achieving a centralization of information and policy-making. Only through full and complete co-ordination can maximum advantage be taken of the complementarities.

Diversification

Many firms and individuals are willing to pay a price for a reduction in the uncertainty or variability associated with their future profit or income. Among the many examples of this is the widespread use of all forms of insurance, which involves the payment of a premium in return for a guarantee against large losses. The insurance companies, by writing a large number of insurance contracts, are able to take advantage of essentially the same sort of complementarity discussed above. They can keep a moderate liquid reserve available to meet current claims while making long-term investments with the remainder of their funds. This basic effect, which might be called complementarity through the reduction in variability of aggregated random phenomena, is also part of the possible payoff to a firm that engages in a policy of diversification. As noted in Chapter I, diversification may be the result of an attempt to utilize some resource the firm finds in excess of its needs. It might, for example, add new products so as to take advantage of existing production facilities, distribution channels, or management skill. Such a policy may, however, bring with it further complementarity if the activities or products grouped together by the firm produce returns that are to some degree random and independent. The resulting reduction in the variability of the firm's income is one of the basic strengths of large diversified firms. They may not be more profitable than small firms, but their profit is more stable and less uncertain. This may be very simply illustrated. Suppose a firm is considering a program of investment in two activities, products, or business undertakings. It has a capital fund in amount X to invest and wonders whether this entire amount should be invested in one activity or in some combination of the two. Would there be some complementary effects if both activities were undertaken? Assume that the firm can undertake either activity at any scale of investment it wishes. It regards the return or profit per dollar invested in activity i as a random variable with mean m_i and standard deviation s_i. In the simplest case these profits are taken to be independent.

Any program of investment consists of investing x in activity 1 and $X - x$ in activity 2. The expected profit from a program is

$$xm_1 + (X - x)m_2$$

and the variance of the profit, considered as a function of x, is

$$\text{Var}(x) = x^2 s_1^2 + (X - x)^2 s_2^2 .$$

For illustration we suppose that $m_1 > m_2$ and $s_1 > s_2$. If the firm wished simply to maximize its expected profit, it would put all of its funds in opportunity 1. If, however, it would like to reduce the variability or uncertainty of its return, it may wish to diversify.[4] That is, it may be willing to sacrifice some of its expected profit in return for a reduction in the variance of its profit.

The variance is a quadratic function of x, which takes a minimum value at

$$x = X \frac{s_2^2}{s_1^2 + s_2^2} .$$

Thus the firm may wish to select a value of x greater than this minimizing value but less than X. If it does so, it will have the program that has the smallest variability for any given expected return or the highest expected return for any given level of variability. To the extent that the returns are correlated, the complementarity will be reduced. This is another case in which, through the aggregation of random phenomena, variability is reduced, and this reduction is of some benefit to the firm.

Centralization of Services and Facilities

These basic effects can be used to touch a fundamental question in organizational design. This is the question of process, as opposed to product, departmentalization that rests on the benefits of complementarity and their relation to the burdens of co-ordination. To design an organization, one must decide which activities are to be performed centrally as services rendered to all the organizational units and which activities are to be decentralized. In the latter case, each organizational unit is given the necessary capability to perform the services for itself. Prominent examples include such staff services as data processing, research, advertising, personnel, and so on. The secretarial pool, the motor pool, and the corporate operations research staff present fundamentally the same problems. For the present we will concentrate only on the question of whether there are complementarities to be realized through centralization or process departmentalization. We will suppress the problems of communication and co-ordination.

Speaking very generally, we suppose there is a service required by the various organizational units of the firm. The complex of people and equipment necessary to provide this service may be organized as a central department or decentralized to each organizational unit. Thus we assume that the facility, the people and equipment, is capable of being subdivided in this way. To take advantage of the basic results of waiting-line theory in this illustration, we make some special assumptions about the needs of the units and the capabilities of the service facility.[5] Each unit generates demands or requests for service in a random fashion. The mean rate at which requests are generated by a unit is d, and the number of requests generated in an interval T is taken to be Poisson-distributed with mean dT. The units are identical in this respect.

With centralized or process-oriented design, we suppose that the service facility performs the requests of the units in the order received, working on them one at a time. The time to complete a request is a random variable having a negative exponential distribution with mean $1/s$. Thus s is the mean rate at which requests can be serviced if the facility operates all of the time. We may then take from waiting-line theory the following results. If there are n organizational units, the proportion of the time that the service facility will be idle is

$$1 - \frac{nd}{s}$$

and the mean time between the submission of a request and completion of service on it is

$$\frac{1}{s - nd}.$$

These results assume that $s > nd$; that is, the service facility is capable of handling the workload imposed upon it.

Consider now a decentralized design or product departmentalization. The service facility used above is divided equally among the units. Each unit then has available the resources to serve its needs, and it is presumed that its resources are not used to serve the needs of other units. In order to emphasize certain effects, we shall assume that the resources available to each unit can accomplish requests at mean rate s/n when fully utilized. This is to assume that the service facilities could be combined, resulting in a productivity that is essentially the sum of their individual productivities. There are many examples of the falsity of such an assumption, in some cases the combined productivity being greater, and in some, less than the sum of the individual values. This implies in part that the delays due to communicating a request from the organizational unit to a central department and the response time of the central department in making its facilities available (if they are free) are negligible.

In a single unit with its own service facilities, those facilities will be idle a proportion of the time given by

$$1 - \frac{d}{s/n} = 1 - \frac{nd}{s}.$$

Thus we would predict that under the assumed conditions the utilization of the service facilities will be the same for the two designs. In other words, there would be no advantage to either design in so far as the proportion of time the facilities are used is concerned. On the other hand, the mean time between the emergence of a request in a unit and its completion by the unit's facilities, or mean delay, is given by

$$\frac{1}{s/n - d} = \frac{n}{s - nd}.$$

Thus for the decentralized design the mean delay increases with n, the number of units. In other terms, the delay reduction advantage in favor of the centralized design increases as the number of units increases. Thus there is clearly a complementarity effect resulting from the grouping of the resources for all of the units together in a central department. The designer has some rough tools here for evaluating the magnitude of this complementarity. It must then be weighed against the effects of delay, communication, and co-ordination that may arise through centralization.

The more interesting case in which the service facility operates in discrete units, working on more than one request at a time, may also be examined with the basic results of waiting-line theory. This may be illustrated using the familiar example of the equipment pool problem.

The Equipment Pool Problem

Consider production in a departmentalized plant in which all requests for materials-handling services can be satisfied by means of a single type of equipment. There are two basic alternatives for controlling and operating the fleet of materials-handling equipment to be used by the plant. One philosophy suggests that all of it should be operated out of a central pool that would receive requests for movement and dispatch equipment to satisfy these requests. The alternative philosophy suggests that equipment should be permanently assigned to each department. The departments would then control their own equipment, which would not ordinarily be used to serve the needs of other departments. Those who argue for the central equipment pool may claim better utilization of the equipment, better service to the departments, and perhaps the possibility of getting by with a smaller fleet. Those who argue for decentralized control in the form of department assignment are, typically, department managers who have had a few bad experiences in getting service from the pool and would very much like to have direct control over their own materials-handling equipment.

In order to make use of elementary waiting-line analysis, we again make the assumption that each department generates materials-handling requests at mean rate d, and that the number of requests in a given period is a Poisson random variable. We assume also that the mean rate at which a fully utilized vehicle completes these requests is s and that the time to accomplish a request is a random variable with a negative exponential distribution. Although the details of the analysis need not be of immediate concern, some interesting hypotheses emerge.[6] As before, it appears that the utilization or the idleness of the equipment will be the same under either policy, but the service rendered by the equipment is better under a centralized, or pool, policy.

In Table 1, the mean delay experienced by a request for movement is given. Mean delay is the average time between the emergence of a request and the beginning of service on it. We assume here that there are as many pieces of equipment as there are departments.

If there is only one department in the plant, there is no policy choice. It appears that as the number of departments in the plant increases, the advantage due to the complementarity of centralization increases at a

TABLE 1

$\frac{d}{s}$	Number of Departments = Number of Vehicles	Mean Delay (Multiples of Mean Service Time)	
		Decentralized	Centralized
.2	1	0.25	0.250
	2		.045
	3		.010
	4		.003
.4	1	.67	.670
	2		.180
	3		.070
	4		.045
.6	1	1.50	1.500
	2		.500
	3		.300
	4		.150
.8	1	4.00	4.000
	2		2.000
	3		1.000
	4		.600

decreasing rate. Here, advantage is measured in terms of reduced mean delay. As the ratio of the mean load on the system d to the mean capacity s increases, the advantage due to centralization becomes less pronounced. In other words, the greater the idle capacity in the system, the greater the advantage of centralization in terms of reduced delay.

Further options are available in the centralized policy in that it may not be necessary to have as many vehicles as there are departments. For example, in the case of $d/s = .2$, the plant could operate with only one vehicle serving four departments. Although this would increase the mean delay to about 4.5 times the mean service time, the resulting saving in vehicles might warrant its consideration.

Horizon of Choice

Still another type of complementarity that can be described in terms of random phenomena results from grouping activities together so that the choices that must be made by management are based upon a wider range of possibilities or selected from a larger list of alternatives. To illustrate this effect, consider a firm that has funds available for capital investment and receives investment proposals from its operating divisions. For simplicity, assume that the investment required is the same for every proposal and that the firm has sufficient funds to engage in only one of the proposed projects. Suppose that the divisions produce these proposals out of similar opportunity environments. We shall take this to mean that the payoff from any proposal may be regarded as a random variable P with probability distribution $f(P)$. Suppose further that the number of proposals submitted, n, increases as the number of operating divisions in the firm is increased.

If the firm has n proposals from which to choose, the expected payoff from the best proposal may be found by solving the expression below for $\bar{P}_{max}$.[7]

$$\int_{P=\bar{P}_{max}}^{\infty} f(P)dP = \frac{1}{n+1}$$

Thus as n increases, the expected payoff from the single best project increases as well; and the firm will, on the average, do better if it has many proposals from which to choose than if it has only a few. The complementarity resulting from this increase in the horizon of choice is of course a part of the explanation for the tendency of large divisionalized forms to centralize the capital-budgeting function. We shall explore this process in some detail in subsequent sections.

Self-containment

To the degree that a unit carries on its functions without co-ordinating them with other organizational units, we say that it is self-contained. This important concept in the design and analysis of organizations has been sometimes referred to as closure, independence, unitization, or informational autonomy. Self-containment or the lack of co-ordination requirements is understood to be relative to the other subunits but not relative to the markets, suppliers, or the environment of the organization.

There is an obvious parallel here between the tactics used by management to cope with a system's complexity in operation and the tactics used by the designer in planning a system. Both look for ways of cutting the system. By this they mean isolating subunits of the total system that can be studied, designed, or managed with minimum necessity for considering the remainder of the system from which the component has been cut. Thus an ideal cutting would identify system components that could be studied in isolation and then reintegrated into the total system with a small number of links, in such a way that the knowledge obtained about the component when studied in isolation remains relevant when it rejoins the system. This is the basic tactic for achieving understanding of complex phenomena.

It is clear that one cannot achieve self-containment simply by isolating an organizational unit from the rest of the units and allowing it to function as it will without regard to the consequences. Self-containment implies something in the way of reasonable effectiveness for the system as a whole. To see what is meant, we consider the following ideal without interpreting it too strictly. Suppose we have a fully operational measure of the effectiveness of the performance of a firm in which full information was available to a central management group. Suppose we consider the effectiveness of the firm when this central management group makes all decisions of consequence or when all decisions are made according to policies laid down by the central group. Suppose now we divide the people, activities, and assets of the firm into subunits. Suppose further that no flow of money, information, people, material, or facilities subsequently occurs among the subunits, except possibly by means of the normal market mechanisms through which these things conventionally pass among independent firms. Suppose also that there exists no agreement in advance among the units as to what activities they will continue to carry on in the future. Now if each subunit formulated its own objectives and set out to pursue them, and if the effectiveness of the system was equal to that of the original centralized system, we would say that the subunits were fully or perfectly self-contained.

Since it would be surprising to discover an interesting system that could be divided into perfectly self-contained subunits, we normally expect some amount of information flow among the subunits. For example, one unit, which we shall call the headquarters unit, will typically place restrictions on the activities of the other subunits. The headquarters unit may do such things as:

1. Specify the objectives to be sought by the subunits (the more operational this specification, the more effective we should expect the result to be in terms of system objectives)

2. Require certain information to be supplied by the subunits and in turn supply information to them

3. Require that the units surrender certain assets (such as cash) and turn to the headquarters unit for their supply of these assets

4. Set down policies that must be followed and standards that must be met by the subunits

5. Establish a system of rewards for the members of the subunits, based perhaps on their performance with relation to the measures for the objectives given in item 1 above

Thus although a fully self-contained unit could presumably continue its existence as an independent business unit without regard for the rest of the firm, in actuality subunits are seldom capable of such independent existence in their original form. Clearly, there is the possibility that a unit might achieve independence by undertaking to provide for itself those things originally provided by the headquarters unit, but this would represent a substantial alteration in the activities of the unit. Note that even in the "holding company" relation between headquarters and the subunits, the headquarters group has some members on the unit's board of directors and requires some cash from the unit in the form of dividends. Thus even here, complete self-containment is not achieved.

Several important implications of the notion of self-containment are worth pointing out. If a unit were fully self-contained, the management of the unit would know that the decisions it made not only did not depend on information as to what other units were doing, but also that the results of these decisions were fully attributable to the unit in question. Thus the performance of a unit could be considered independent of the performance of other units. This would mean:

1. That the management of a unit could be held accountable for the results achieved by their unit, and that they could reasonably be rewarded according to this performance

2. That the management of the unit could learn effectively from their experience, since in relating decisions to results they would not have to take into account what was going on in the other units

Thus complete self-containment would suggest the possibility of a desirable immediacy between action and reward, and the possibility for a direct accountability for performance. Further, it would make the problem of organizational learning simpler, and thus, presumably, more effective. As we shall see, organizational learning, which is vital to the progress of any organization, turns out to play a central role in a decentralized structure. In using transfer prices, for example, to co-ordinate the activities of subunits of the firm, the learning process plays the role of co-ordinator, and the effectiveness of this process is directly related to the rapidity with which the decentralized system approaches the stability of optimal operations.[8]

Interdependence

When the way in which one activity is carried on influences the cost of performing another activity, the two are said to be interdependent. To make the concept of "complementarity" operational, one would wish to specify the way in which an activity is carried on in terms of the resources consumed (including time) and the quantity and quality of its output. Similarly, cost is used here in the most general sense to denote the money, manpower, plant, capacity, and material used in an activity.

If two activities are interdependent, their joint performance usually requires co-ordination. That is, unless they are carried on in a co-ordinated fashion, the interdependence may produce unfavorable, higher cost results, or one may fail to realize the full advantage of their complementarities. Co-ordination implies that in planning how one activity is to be undertaken, one must consider how others will be performed. Thus interdependence becomes equivalent to lack of self-containment when the interdependent activities are performed by different organizational units. The designer may well seek to group the most interdependent activities together in organizational units in order to take greatest advantage of the complementarities, while at the same time keeping down the costs of providing the necessary co-ordination. However, because of the cognitive limitations of the manager who must carry on the co-ordination function, there is a limit beyond which an organizational unit may not grow if the co-ordination is to remain effective. Thus the inevitable result is that try as one will to group into units activities that are interdependent, there will remain interdependencies among the activities in differing organizational units. The units can seldom be made completely self-contained.

Interdependence is very much a matter of degree. Perhaps it is nearly always possible to identify some interdependence, however weak, between two activities. For example, a plant on the West Coast producing product A and a plant on the East Coast producing product B may be thought of as drawing labor from the country's work force. A man working in one plant cannot simultaneously be employed in the other. Thus the level of employment in plant A may have some very distant influence on the cost of labor in plant B. Yet what we are interested in is the sort of interdependence that has consequences potentially important enough to warrant co-ordination and can be deliberately designed into the system so as to take advantage of complementarities.

Generally speaking, one may identify two types of interdependence. Two units may be interdependent if there is interaction between their inputs or their outputs.

Input interdependence arises when two units share, or compete for, common commodities or services. Labor, materials, or capital obtained from outside the firm by two units may produce interdependence through the economies of large-quantity purchasing or the diseconomies that arise when consumption by one unit raises the prices paid by the other. Two units may also receive products, capital, staff services, long-range plans, managerial skills, and so on, from a common source inside the firm. Not to be overlooked, of course, is interdependence that arises when two units share a common source of information, ideas, policies, and innovations.

Units may also be interdependent through interaction of their outputs, perhaps selling in a common market or sharing in the satisfaction of common requirements. The output of one unit influences the price paid to, or the quantity demanded of, the other unit.

Finally, of course, we may combine these two types of interdependence to include the case in which the output of one organizational unit becomes the input of another.

Communication

The basic effort of the organizational designer is to group together into units those activities that are complementary and that require the greatest amount of co-ordination for their effective performance. The greater the degree of self-containment of these subunits, the less the burden of communication and co-ordination among them. Thus the problem is to group activities so as to take advantage of complementarities, while balancing the resulting savings against the increasing costs of co-ordination necessitated by the residue of interdependence among units. The underlying premise is that communication and co-ordination within an organizational unit are less costly than among organizational units. Co-ordination must be broadly defined here to include more than the formulation and administration of plans for the units. It may be essentially an activity that communicates information among the units but permits them to make their own responses to the information. Alternatively, co-ordination may essentially perform the function of reducing to a reasonable number the alternatives among which a unit must choose.

The designer seeks to develop organizational arrangements that take advantage of the differences in the ease of communication among various organizational channels. These differences are to be understood partly in terms of cognitive effects that stem from the limitations of the human participants and partly in terms of motivational effects that bear upon the incentive to communicate.

Cognitive Effects

It has already been noted that mere size alone may not produce a communication burden that will limit the scale of operations of the firm. Although growth may lead to the establishment of a functional organization, and this in turn may alter the co-ordination problems faced by the firm, they do not become really crucial until some diversity of operations develops. Indeed, a large volume of similar activities can be rather easily co-ordinated through the development of broad policies and standards for their conduct. Diversity—for example, diversity in products, markets, and technology—seems to have been the fundamental challenging factor in showing organizational inadequacies. The attempt to deal with diverse operations on the basis of broad policies leads to increasingly unsatisfactory results. This relation between the breadth or scope of a policy and the diversity of operations to which it must be applied is a basic one that we shall shortly examine in more detail. The obvious response of the organization designer is to group similar activities into subunits, thus effectively reducing the "cognitive strain" on the managers of the units and permitting them to deal in detail with the operations of the subunit.

In this connection it may be noted that the advent of highly refined data-processing systems has reduced communication delays and greatly increased the volume of information that may be stored and transmitted. These systems by themselves have not, however, altered the cognitive capabilities of those who must ultimately use the information as a basis for decision. Only by being increasingly selective in the information considered by a decision-maker and by efforts to routinize and thus delegate some of his decisions can we make better use of his capabilities. Although these cognitive factors are basic, it is perhaps equally useful for the designer to consider the incentives that participants in the organization have to communicate.

Motivational Effects

An organizational unit has been defined in part by suggesting that communication within the unit is "easier" than communication among units. One might raise several hypotheses that shed light on these effects, primarily in motivational terms. The easier communication within units may be the result of such factors as:

1. The members of an organizational unit are more likely to share a perception of a common, immediate, and operational set of goals. Thus each person's needs for information are more clearly understood, and the rewards and penalties for meeting these needs tend to be more direct and personal.

2. Long and close association among unit members, coupled with their shared goals, will tend to make their communications more effective. They may operate in a highly co-ordinated fashion but require less information less frequently transmitted because they have come to be good predictors of each other's behavior.

3. One would expect that communication within a unit would be more frequent, more rapid, and less costly. Unit members would be expected to have more opportunity for informal communication. On the other hand, communication among units tends to become formalized in the sense of filling out standard forms and so on. This formalization increases the cost of communication, slows it down, reduces the voluntary incentive to communicate, and results in the

loss of a good deal of information through the "coding" processes involved. It is difficult to design formal communication systems that can transmit the subtleties of expert judgments, the intangible considerations, or the uncertainties present.

4. Within a unit there is less motivation to deliberately bias information, and it is easier to check for possible biases.

Generally speaking, one would hypothesize that communication within a unit will be enhanced to the degree that the unit has a well-defined operational goal. Indeed, one of the essential objectives of organizational design is to establish units that have clear goals, can see their own attainments, and can be held fully accountable for their results. This is the fundamental difficulty of the functional organization. Each of the functional units finds difficulty in establishing operational goals, and headquarters in turn finds it nearly impossible to fix the responsibility of any unit for the results achieved by the firm. Indeed, functional units tend to evolve their own goals that deviate from those of the firm. In such a situation the need for co-ordination is great, the tendency is for decisions to be highly centralized, and the functional units often find it to their advantage to introduce bias in the information they produce.

Bias and Reliability

In an organization having, say, several divisions and a headquarters group, bias and unreliability effects may be expected to emerge. The data required of the divisions by headquarters may, in their opinion, serve no purpose they understand or care about. Thus requests from headquarters for information are treated as nuisances, and little effort may be expended to provide reliable responses. Indeed, the divisional responses may be the roughest sorts of estimates, since without some understanding of the uses to be made of the information, it is difficult for them to decide the appropriate degree of reliability to seek. Because they see no usefulness in the resulting data, they are moved to respond with the minimum of effort that they judge will be acceptable to headquarters. This effect becomes more serious when headquarters, knowing how difficult it is to get information and having no notion of its reliability, adopts these rough estimates as certainties and treats them as established truths.

Perhaps even more troublesome is the motivation that may tempt the divisions to introduce deliberate biases into their communications to headquarters. On the one hand, the divisions compete with each other for certain resources such as capital and, unless they can be held accountable, may find it to their advantage to distort their justifications for capital requirements. On the other hand, they may simply tell headquarters what they think it wants to hear about their operations, especially if there appears little possibility that their reports will be verified. Thus in the worst cases the central management group tends to become a sort of "informational captive" of the divisions.

There are two general sorts of responses to these problems of bias and reliability in communication among organizational units. On the one hand, efforts may be made to eliminate these effects by

1. Making an independent determination of the statements made by the divisions, either routinely or on a sampling basis

2. Establishing mechanisms by which divisional estimates are ultimately compared with actual events, say, through such procedures as post-auditing of capital investments

3. Discounting divisional statements, for example, by cutting their budget request by some amount or refusing a certain number of their requests for various resources (these are forms of "fine tuning" the organization by overstressing it)

On the other hand, one may try to offer a positive incentive to the divisions to provide good information. This is particularly difficult, for it means designing a mechanism that makes it clear to the divisions that it is to their own advantage to furnish good-quality information to headquarters. For example, it may be suggested that divisional managers have a positive incentive to provide good information because such information does in fact increase the profitability of the firm as a whole, and the rewards of division managers are in part based on the firm's profitability. This is a part of the most difficult problem of designing objectives for divisions that are consistent with the firm's objectives.

The Suppression of Risk

As soon as an organization grows large enough to benefit from a division of labor in decision-making, it becomes necessary to have some means of expressing the risk and uncertainty involved in decisions. This need arises when parts of the decision-making process are delegated to others or to computers. Yet it surely is one of the most widely observed facts of organizational life that risk and uncertainty are not made explicit; indeed, they are suppressed to an overwhelming degree. When information is passed from one organizational unit to another, very often all the variability in the data is omitted in favor of summarizing parameters. Expert and informed judgments of risk and uncertainty are lost when opinions are required and expressed as certainties. Managers deal with risk-taking situations in terms of their "best estimates" of the quantities involved, neglecting the uncertainties. A rough order-of-magnitude guess by someone becomes an accepted figure in the process of organizational choice. In fact, one might almost imagine that the more uncertainty associated with some estimate, the less the tendency of the organization to recognize anything except the single valued expression of the estimate.

The explicit expression of risk in large organizations would facilitate (1) communication for purposes of co-ordination; (2) delegation of parts of the decision-making process; (3) planning the information-gathering activities of the firm; and (4) learning, teaching, and checking the subtle process of blending mature business judgment with explicit data that occurs when a decision is made.

There are several plausible hypotheses that help to understand the suppression of risk. Managers who have no explicit way of dealing with risk in their choice processes may wish to suppress it. To acknowledge it would require an explanation of how it is considered in making a decision. Lacking such a plan for explicitly considering risk, the manager might find himself on the verge of admitting that his decisions were somewhat irrational.

The suppression of risk allows the organization to communicate and reason in the language of certainty, and this mode of expression may be attractive for several reasons.

1. Certainty represents the traditional academic view of many business decisions, and this may reflect a tendency to fit things into academic formulas and modes of thought.

2. Certainty may be associated with personality characteristics such as boldness, aggressiveness, confidence, success, self-assurance, and feelings of power.

3. Certainty is surely related in part to the lack of language for thinking about and expressing uncertainty noted before.

4. Certainty may be a part of an individual's need to preserve a self-image of the assured, confident, and successful man of affairs.

5. Certainty may in part explain the appeal to all manner of hunches, cues, habits, and rules of thumb with which a decision model may be simplified.

6. Most important, certainty may help to explain some of the non-rational relationships psychologists have pointed out between evidence, experience, and beliefs. Facts alone are seldom sufficient to change people's minds.

We are dealing here with a widely observed human tendency to convert assumptions into facts, doubts into certainties, and to revise images of decision situations so as to meet the need for certainty.

Perhaps one of the more interesting reasons why managers may seldom deal with risk explicitly is the insufficiency of language in which to express it. In order to make statements operational, one relies heavily on the language he has available. Clearly, managers recognize decisions made in the face of risk and speak about more or less risky future events. To translate these remarks into operational hypotheses, one must have within his vocabulary the concept of probability, which is the means by which science makes risk operational. In other words, the predictive content of statements involving ideas of risk can only be specified by giving directions for the measurement of risk. The interpretation of probability theory in terms of events in the conduct of business affairs is essentially the specification of a set of operations for measuring risk.

One would hypothesize that the terms "probability," "risk," and "the law of averages" are, in the ordinary usage of the person untrained in the theory and interpretation of probability, not fully operational. Thus the manager who holds no operational conception of risk is at considerable disadvantage when it comes to making explicit his reasoning in risk-taking decisions.

These hypotheses lead one directly to a consideration of the Bayesian approach to decisions as a possibility both for providing a language and a logic for handling risk. There is much interest in Bayesian ideas at present, since they give highly intuitive results and offer appealing explanations of a number of things one sees in actual management situations. In a subsequent section these ideas will be applied to a particular problem to illustrate some of their possibilities.[9]

One might suggest some hypotheses about organizational design on the basis of these considerations. For example:

1. The greater the uncertainty associated with a decision, the more difficult it will be to communicate the necessary information about it.

2. The greater the uncertainty that characterizes a decision, the greater the tendency for it to be delegated.

3. The greater the uncertainty associated with an estimate, the greater the tendency for the division making the estimate to absorb or suppress it.

4. Delegation of decisions involving considerable risk and uncertainty is particularly difficult because (a) it is difficult to communicate the attitudes toward risk held by the headquarters management, and (b) it is difficult to design a system that delegates risky decisions and provides, at the same time, a means of holding the decision-maker fairly accountable for his performance in the face of risk and uncertainty.

Reducing the Burden of Co-ordination

As has been indicated, one of the central tasks of the organizational designer is to reduce the burden of co-ordination. He may do this in part by the way in which he groups activities into subunits. He seeks to establish objectives for the subunits such that if each works toward its own particular goals, two effects will follow. The achievement of unit goals will contribute to the achievement of firm goals. Further, the subunits will be self-contained in the sense that they may proceed toward their own objectives without having to take account of what is being done in other units. Much of the discussion that follows will be directed toward this most difficult end.

In addition, there are a variety of methods that may be utilized to make co-ordination among units more or less automatic, and thus reduce the cost of achieving it. Perhaps the most interesting of these is the notion of transfer prices. A price system is designed to operate between the units, which are supposed to seek maximization of their own profits. The price system is supposed to achieve a co-ordination of supply and demand within the firm much like that it is supposed to achieve in an economic system. Further, there are actions a designer may consider that tend to reduce the burden of co-ordination, largely by making the behavior of the subunits more predictable.

These actions involve all manner of standardized methods and procedures that greatly restrict the freedom of the units, yet at the same time make their performance more predictable and thus less in need of explicit co-ordination. These standardized responses are the means of knowing in advance what a division's action will be in a particular situation, and restricting the possible actions to a reasonable number, thus reducing the variety in divisional behavior. It includes also a suppression of the divisions' freedom, motivation, and ability to innovate. The development of such methods involves a choice between broad general policies designed to fix a division's response for a wide variety of instances and a larger number of more precisely defined policy categories such that each instance receives a more nearly appropriate individual response. The greater the number of policy categories, the greater the effectiveness with which situations are handled. On the other hand, it is more expensive to design, administer, and co-ordinate the results of the greater number of policies. These trade-offs suggest as an area of some consequence for the organization designer the rational design of policy categories.

The principles may be illustrated in terms of a simple example. Suppose the firm encounters a population of situations, each of which is characterized by a value of a single variable s. The designer regards s as a random variable for purposes of designing appropriate policy. Let r stand for the response of the firm in a given situation, and suppose that the cost of this response is measured by $(r - s)^2$.

We assume further that the situations are encountered by the operating divisions of the firm, but that the necessary skill, experience, and knowledge for making an individual response to each situation is possessed only by those at the headquarters level. The designer may wish to consider making such skills available within each division or transmitting information about each situation to headquarters so that the appropriate individual response may be communicated back. We suppose that instead of these plans, the first of which involves costly duplication and the second of which involves costly communication, the designer considers a third type of scheme.

The divisions are instructed that when a situation is encountered that has some observable characteristic s, their response is to be r_c if $s_c \leqq s \leqq s_{c+1}$. Here c takes the values 1, 2, . . . N, and N is the number of policy categories. The implication is that if N is small, the r_c can be carefully spelled out by the headquarters group and executed by the divisions with a minimum of specialized skill and knowledge. Further, it is supposed that the policy categories tend to assure that the divisions' activity contributes toward the objectives of the firm.

For simplicity, assume that the divisions can observe s directly. One plan is to take $N = 1$, which is to require that all situations be given the same response, r_1. In such a case one might wish to choose r_1 so as to minimize the expected cost of the responses; that is, $E(r_1 - s)^2$. This can be done of course, by choosing r_1 equal to the expected value of s, and the resulting cost will be given by the variance of s. The next step might be to have $N = 2$. In this case the expected value of the cost would be

$$V(r_1, r_2, s_2) = \int_{s = s_1}^{s_2} (r_1 - s)^2 f(s) ds + \int_{s = s_2}^{s_3} (r_2 - s)^2 f(s) ds$$

where $V(r_1, r_2, s_2) =$ the expected cost of a plan having parameters r_1, r_2, and s_2, and $f(s) =$ the probability distribution of s.

Here the designer wishes to choose the parameters so as to minimize the value of the cost function V. In the simple case in which $f(s)$ is uniform over the range $a \leqq s \leqq b$, appropriate values would be

$$r_1 = (a + b)/4$$

$$r_2 = 3(a + b)/4$$

$$s_2 = (a + b)/2$$

The designer may consider increasing N and the resulting decreases in cost as optimal policy categories are established.

We are supposing that if the divisions responded without guidance from headquarters, their response to a situation s would be $r = s + e$, where e is a random variable. To say that the divisions lack the necessary skill and experience is to say that the cost of permitting the division to respond is large. This cost is measured by the variance of e. Perhaps also it is important to know at headquarters what responses are being made. Suppose r represents a resource consumed in the response, and headquarters wishes to predict the demand for this resource. Given that k situations are encountered, the variance in the amount of resource used is expressed by $\mathrm{Var}(r|k)$.

1. If the divisions respond without guidance,
   $\mathrm{Var}(r|k) = k\,\mathrm{Var}(s) + k\,\mathrm{Var}(e)$.

2. If headquarters responds to each situation individually and without error $(r = s)$,
   $\mathrm{Var}(r|k) = k\,\mathrm{Var}(s)$.

3. If a single policy category is used,
   $\mathrm{Var}(r|k) = 0$.

4. If N policy categories are used, let

   $p_j =$ the probability that a situation falls in the jth policy category

   $\sum_j p_j r_j = \bar{r} =$ average amount of r consumed in a response

   $\sum_j (r_j - \bar{r})^2 p_j = \mathrm{Var}(r,N) =$ variance of the amount of r used in a particular response when there are N categories

   Thus, given N categories
   $\mathrm{Var}(r|k) = k\,\mathrm{Var}(r,N)$.

Thus the designer might consider balancing the effects of the cost of responses, cost of communication, cost of designing and implementing policy categories, and the resulting predictability of system behavior.

Illustrating the Basic Concepts

The fundamental ideas of complementarity, co-ordination, self-containment, and interdependence can provide only a conceptual structure for considering problems of organizational design. We turn next to the application of these concepts to a specific set of problems in an attempt to make them somewhat more operational. The problems of designing capital-budgeting systems have been chosen for this purpose. Capital budgeting is one of the areas in which major firms have been conscious of their degree of centralization or decentralization, and have been most explicit in their policies for delegation. In large organizations, capital control is one of the central mechanisms by which the top management group retains control over the long range of destiny of the firm, yet leaves to the divisional managements control of the daily affairs of the business. It is also a likely choice because there is considerable data available on what is being done in industry. In the next several chapters we examine in some detail the problems of designing capital-budgeting systems.

1. Chandler, *op. cit.*, pp. 284–98.

2. See for example Robert Schlaifer, *Introduction to Statistics for Business Decisions* (New York: McGraw-Hill Book Co., 1961), p. 320.

3. K. S. Krishnan and V. R. K. Rao, "Inventory Control in N Warehouses," *Journal of Industrial Engineering*, XVI, No. 3 (May–June, 1965), 212–15.

4. For full development and application of these ideas see Harry Markowitz, *Portfolio Selection: Efficient Diversification of Investments* (New York: John Wiley & Sons, 1959) and D. E. Farrar, *The Investment Decision under Uncertainty* (Englewood Cliffs, N.J.: Prentice-Hall, 1962).

5. See any basic reference on waiting-line theory; for example, Philip M. Morse, *Queues, Inventories, and Maintenance* (New York: John Wiley & Sons, 1958).

6. This is based on a direct application of the single- and multiple-channel models. It has been fully worked out in W. T. Morris, *Analysis for Materials Handling Management* (Homewood, Ill.: Richard D. Irwin, 1962), pp. 98–105.

7. Alexander M. Mood, *Introduction to the Theory of Statistics* (New York: McGraw-Hill Book Co., 1950), pp. 385–87.

8. See Chapter IX.

9. See Chapter V.

CHAPTER 3

CAPITAL-BUDGETING SYSTEMS

Design Problems

Out of the evidence available on capital-budgeting systems now in use, we have attempted to extract some problems that relate generally to the degree of decentralization involved and serve to illustrate the basic ideas of the previous chapter. The general plan is to hypothesize some major design questions from the data, to formulate models that reflect roughly the ways in which these problems are handled in practice, and then to use the models to suggest directions in which the organization designer might look for improvements. In developing the models, three general objectives were considered most important:

1. The models should be simple and transparent. This means that many refinements in notation and computation remain to be accomplished. It seemed more important that the models used at this stage of investigation impart some understanding of the phenomena rather than express in elegant form the complex details of reality.

2. The models should reflect, and to some degree explain, the ways in which capital budgeting is carried on in actual organizations. Here

we are of necessity concerned with gross qualitative effects. One purpose of these models is to suggest the sort of data that does not now appear to be available but that seems necessary to understand the basic issues arising in the design of a capital-budgeting system. In this sense the models attempt to produce interesting hypotheses rather than to establish conclusions.

3. At the level of observation employed, different organizations appear to carry on their capital-budgeting tasks in rather different ways. Thus it is necessary to have systems of models that try to account for the various ways of doing things. Although it is not possible to use these models to say unequivocally that one capital-budgeting system is better than another, some effort has been devoted to raising hypotheses as to how a system might be improved and as to certain specific ways in which one sort of system might be better than another.

In this section the data on some aspects of the capital-budgeting process that we wish to reflect in the analysis is outlined. These aspects have to do both with the general nature of the process (whether, for example, projects are funded continuously or in batches), and with the degree of decentralization (for example, what size projects may be undertaken by an operating division without the approval of headquarters). The major empirical features we wish to consider are these:

1. That capital budgeting may be to some extent decentralized and that this may have interesting consequences for the way in which it is carried out.

2. That it is a process involving more than the restricted decision problems usually discussed in the capital-budgeting literature. It includes:

    a) Search for investment opportunities

    b) Evaluation of these opportunities

    c) Prediction of capital availability

    d) The actual choice of investments

    e) Post-auditing of past investments

3. That it involves managerial judgment at many points. This has been reflected in part by:

    a) Providing for the explicit introduction of judgments into the model

    b) Noting at several points that a highly refined optimizing analysis of a decision problem would in actuality often be suppressed in favor of judgments that reflect the general nature of the considerations involved, but not their precise details

c) Leaving open in the analysis a number of things that at present can perhaps best find expression in judgments (for example, the effect of a time delay on the funding of a given project, or the decision-making workload that can be effectively handled by a group of executives)

We have drawn on a number of empirical studies of capital budgeting in order to ground the analysis in fact. However, it is not to be expected that all aspects of the process reported in these studies are captured in the analysis. Simple models are necessarily the result of abstraction on a selective basis. The basis in this case is frankly to get at the considerations that seem to be most relevant in considering problems of centralization and decentralization.[1]

Central Control

Historically, the capital-budgeting function has been more centralized than decentralized. This tradition can be viewed in a most interesting fashion in terms of the history of a large organization such as the General Motors Corporation.[2] The basic issues that emerged early in the evolution of General Motors include the following:

1. Central control of the firm's funds is one of the basic sources of strength for a large firm. In the short run, central cash control permits most effective use of the firm's cash and gives the divisions access to potentially greater cash resources than might be the case if they were individual firms. Central control of funds for long-term investment is the major source of the headquarters group's power to influence the destiny of the firm. It can choose among a large and diversified group of investment opportunities, seeking to make the best use of the funds from an organizational rather than from a divisional point of view. Thus the firm has the complementarity of greater financial strength than would be possessed by the "sum of its individual divisions."

2. This central control, however, raises the need for making explicit estimates of costs and benefits to be expected from capital investments and expressing these in a manner that permits comparison among the proposals submitted by the various divisions. It also raises the need for some sort of check on the statements made by the divisions in support of their proposals and some scheme for at least roughly controlling the expenditure of investment funds and matching the results achieved with the predictions made.

3. Central control over capital budgeting solves directly the problem of co-ordinating the investment plans of the divisions among themselves and co-ordinating these plans with the availability of funds for the firm.

4. The firm may elect central control of capital budgeting as a primary means of finding out and controlling what is going on in the divisions. That is, it may be centralized less out of intrinsic necessity than out of a choice of capital budgeting as a primary means of organizational control. Certainly, long-range planning, if it exists in a firm, is likely to be highly centralized, and capital-budgeting control may be the basic means of implementing the strategic, long-range plans.

5. On the other side of the coin, factors that impel the firm toward some degree of decentralization in capital budgeting were clear very early as well. These include:

a) The need to avoid using up the energies of the headquarters group on a large number of small capital proposals.

b) The "rubber stamp" effect; the uselessness of submitting to headquarters certain proposals that are generally agreed to be essential and well justified. If headquarters routinely approves such proposals, they might well be handled at the operating levels.

c) The presence of information and judgments at the operating level that cannot be effectively communicated to the higher levels. For example, it is traditional to suppress most of the uncertainty associated with an investment proposal when it is written up for transmission. Indeed, there is seldom a conventional, effective means of expressing this uncertainty. The headquarters group must either supply its own judgments of uncertainty or neglect those uncertainty considerations evident at the operating levels. This tends to place a premium on using decision-makers at headquarters that have some familiarity with divisional problems.

d) Decentralizing the capital-budgeting process may be closely associated with the incentive aspects of decentralization in general. Thus when a division manager is instructed to take the responsibility for his division in a manner approaching the responsibility of an entrepreneur, capital budgeting should be included to some extent. If his rewards are related to his achievements, then presumably his responsibility and authority must include a significant range of investment decisions.

e) The time required for a proposal to reach headquarters and for a decision to be returned may be substantial. Thus the need to give the firm a quicker reaction time (or short gestation period on proposals) impels one toward some degree of decentralization.

6. Finally, out of these conflicting considerations, it is not surprising that organizations should emerge that are neither highly centralized nor highly decentralized. The better organizational designs seem to lie somewhere between the two extremes. When such a need for a "mixed" system exists, one may well expect to find that the evolutionary process by which the organization seeks a workable design is a more extended one than would be the case if the optimum lay in one of the purer forms of organization, either highly centralized or highly decentralized. Coupled with this one may also expect the phenomenon of "hunting" to occur.

Planning Horizon

Studies of the capital-budgeting process exhibit considerable agreement on the point that forward planning of capital investments extends typically a few months to a year in the future. Beyond this horizon capital-investment plans may exist, but they tend to be incomplete and taper off as one goes further and further into the future. This horizon applies to capital-investment plans themselves. Clearly, an investment considered today has consequences often extending several years into the future, and thus the investment must be supported and justified by predictions extending over its useful life.

A highly rational analysis of current investment opportunities should consider not only the opportunities and funds available in the current period but also (1) funds expected to become available in future periods, (2) future outlays and incomes expected to result from commitments to current opportunities, and (3) future opportunities that may become available.

In the interests of simplicity we have suppressed this and considered only the opportunities and the funds currently available. This is to some extent justified by the empirical evidence indicating that plans for capital investments are not in fact made very far into the future. It is further supported by the fact that both through increasing uncertainty and decreasing present value events tend to diminish in their importance for current decisions as one moves further into the future. It is possible, too, that a major investment in future planning would be made by the central agency of a large firm and not replicated by any of its decentralized divisions. If this occurs, it is reasonable to suppose that under decentralized operation the central agency will make available to the divisions the results of its long-range planning activities. Thus to a considerable extent divisional decisions would be based on information similar to that used for centralized decisions. One might then expect the differences between centralized and decentralized operations to be influenced in a minor way by the degree of forward planning considered.

Predictions extending into the future are of reduced importance for two conventional reasons that appear to operate as partial explanations of the tendency toward a short planning horizon. The first of these is the traditional discount for futurity, based on the notion that a dollar today is worth more than a dollar tomorrow. Given an interest rate at which funds may be invested, the present worth of future sums may be calculated by the conventional discounting process. The other form of "discounting" is for uncertainty. It is typically the case that the further into the future an event, the greater the uncertainty associated with it in the conception of a decision-maker. If the event is a money income, then the greater the uncertainty, the less the utility of the income to a risk-averse decision-maker. Thus future incomes, having considerable uncertainty and therefore low utility, cannot compete for the attention of the decision-maker in the face of near-term incomes with less uncertainty and higher utility. In the models that follow, a near-term planning horizon is implied together with a discount for futurity, resulting in an investment opportunity being considered in terms of its present worth. In addition, the mechanism for independently expressing uncertainty and taking actions to reduce uncertainty is provided.

Search

In considering the process of searching for investment opportunities, we may first set aside those opportunities that thrust themselves upon the firm and are essential to preserving the basic existence of the business. For example, a major component of the production process fails, and an investment must be made to repair or replace it. Little search is involved, and little choice remains given that production is to continue. Moving beyond such opportunities, we consider cases that present the firm with greater need for discretion. The following hypotheses about search have been more or less roughly reflected in the analysis:

1. Some firms find that an ample supply of investment opportunities seems to arise in the natural course of business affairs, and thus the extent of search effort is not a matter of deliberate policy. In other situations deliberate decisions are made with respect to the amount and nature of the resources devoted to searching for investment opportunities.

2. Although investment proposals may arise from any level in the firm, the analysis generally assumes that deliberate search efforts are carried on by the operating divisions, and that the opportunities for investment discovered fall essentially within the scope of the activities of these divisions. The

discovery of a potential opportunity does not generally produce sufficient certainty as to its consequences; thus further investigation may follow both at the divisional level and at headquarters.

3. Search, especially in the sense of research, is a highly uncertain undertaking that must often be justified on the vaguest of grounds. We have tried to reflect this by considering the opportunity environment within which search is being carried out to be an uncertain one. As is usually the case, we do not necessarily suppose that those who plan search activities think of it explicitly in this fashion. They must think of it somehow if search is a considered decision, and a probabilistic model permits one to capture and explain some of the basic empirical features of the process.

4. In considering the opportunity environment, we suppose that a limited planning horizon is used, roughly in agreement with the limitations of the planning horizon for investment opportunities. Thus search is basically aimed at finding opportunities that could be taken up in the near future rather than with opportunities that could be used only in the distant future. This is not to suppose that the latter sort of opportunities will be overlooked when they are discovered, but simply that immediate proposals are the main focus of attention in the search process.

5. The motivation to search or to terminate search we take to be essentially a "satisficing" process. That is, search is carried on until a project is discovered that meets some criteria defining a satisfactory or acceptable project. Though it is possible in certain situations to define these criteria in such a way that search is terminated when the expected marginal gain is equal to the expected marginal cost, we do not insist on this degree of rationality except as a guide toward the tendency of a firm's search policy.

6. Two basic kinds of opportunities are considered, transitory and persistent. A transitory opportunity is one that becomes available but if not taken up within a short period of time, disappears. Thus the changing market price of a stock offers a transitory opportunity for investment. A persistent opportunity is one that is available for a longer period of time. Indeed, we will suppose that a persistent opportunity may be taken up any time within the firm's planning horizon.

7. In cases where search policy is a matter of deliberation, we will suppose that:

   a) The extent of search is roughly matched to the supply of funds available or potentially available to the firm, within the planning horizon.

   b) The process of search, evaluation, and investment decision may be either a sequential process or a batch process. In the sequential case it is assumed that these three steps are carried out with respect to a given investment proposal, and then the firm moves on to a subsequent search, evaluation, and decision sequence on another opportunity. In the batch case one might suppose that search is carried on until a group of opportunities is discovered. These are then evaluated and investment decisions made relative to the to the group.

Evaluation

We have supposed that a proposal reaches the decision stage by going through two previous stages. First, it must be discovered. It is assumed that the decision to undertake search carries with it an implicit commitment to find out at least some basic features of an opportunity, not simply to identify its existence. This is to say, search and discovery involve some evaluation or uncertainty reduction. Just how much information-gathering is thus implicit in search is not a major concern in the analysis. It is supposed, however, that there is a point at which deliberate consideration is given to gathering more information about a proposal. The choice is made as to whether the proposal is sufficiently well understood to warrant no further efforts toward uncertainty reduction, or whether further evaluation is called for prior to the decision step. Wherever this point comes, it separates the search process from the evaluation process. Of course, evaluation once undertaken may itself be a sequential process in which the question is repeatedly faced, "Has sufficient evaluation been undertaken, or is more required?"

Explicit consideration of the extent of evaluation effort in connection with a given proposal does not seem to exist to any great extent in actual practice. Presumably, the amount of evaluative effort is determined implicitly by the judgments of the analysts, the demands of management, and perhaps some conventions that have grown up in the firm. In order to explore the process, we have tried to understand it by means of an explicit analysis involving such considerations as

1. The need for evaluation arises essentially out of the subjective uncertainty that surrounds a proposal. This uncertainty is seldom precisely expressed and often entirely implicit. We have provided a mechanism in the form of a Bayesian model within which this uncertainty can be expressed and considered.

2. Subjective uncertainty and its reduction imply a healthy content of what must be called management judgment. It is clear that management judgments play an extensive role in the evaluation and decision steps, and thus must to some crude extent be reflected in the models.

3. Subjective uncertainty typically tends to increase with futurity.

4. In the absence of a customary and effective way of expressing uncertainty, the impressions held at division level can be only very imperfectly transmitted to higher levels. Indeed, through lack of effective means of expression, through management demands for certainty, or through conventional reluctance to admit uncertainty, these considerations may be suppressed or absorbed at division level.

5. A proposal is often subjected to reviews at various levels of the organization, at which time other inputs of management judgment take place.

6. Modern utility theory considers the value of an undertaking to be dependent in part on the uncertainty associated with it. We have not attempted to reflect this explicitly in the analysis, although one could do so. Thus policies for diversification are not directly considered here.

7. The evaluation of a project is directed toward the reduction of the uncertainty associated with some explicit criteria. There is considerable diversity both as to what criteria for budgeting decisions are and what they ought to be. Rules of thumb involving rate of return, payout period, discounted cash flow, and so on are common. For simplicity, we have chosen to consider as an explicit criterion the present worth of a proposal, based upon an interest rate and planning horizon that are assumed to be given by the firm. The analysis does not really depend upon this assumption, and other criteria and associated rules of thumb might easily be substituted for this present worth.

Delegation

As pointed out earlier, mixed systems neither highly centralized nor highly decentralized have tended to evolve in practice. Where such partial delegation of the capital-investment decision occurs, two general patterns appear. The first and most important is delegation on the basis of the size of the initial investment required in a project. One large firm permits any investment of $25,000 to be approved at divisional level, but larger proposals must be decided at higher levels. A wide variety of such size criteria is evident. Indeed, one of the main points of the analysis that follows is to suggest the results to be expected from varying such a delegation criterion.[3]

The second pattern of delegation is based on a classification of expenditures into categories such as:

Maintenance

Repair

Cost reduction

Expansion

Replacement

Some of these categories may be delegated to divisional levels, but others may require a headquarters decision. Delegation in this case may be based on the notion that certain categories of expenditure are clearly essential and thus the headquarters decision would be simply a "rubber stamp" action. It may also be based on principles such as:

1. Permitting the divisions to decide on proposals clearly very profitable or very unprofitable

2. Delegating to the divisions those classes of decisions characterized by low uncertainty, routinized methods of evaluation, and standard decision-making processes

3. Delegating to the divisions the decisions that can be characterized by operational goals, whereas those in which the goals lack operationality are reserved to headquarters

Budget Dynamics

There is a general indication in the empirical evidence on the capital-budgeting process that some firms usually are faced with more opportunities to invest than they are able to fund with capital from sources they are willing to consider. Yet in other firms there appear to be fewer projects available than the number that the firm is financially able to undertake, and the firm may have a substantial and accumulating liquid-asset position. We have called the former situation the "ample projects" case and the latter the "ample funds" case. In the ample funds case it is reasonable to suppose that the firm's planning horizon may extend more than the usual distance into the future and that liquid assets are being accumulated for some undertaking dimly seen and anticipated in the more distant future.

There is evidence also that some firms fund proposals more or less continuously as they arise, whereas other firms accumulate the proposals into batches before funding decisions are made. We have called the former policy simply continuous budgeting; the latter is referred to as batch budgeting. Various rules for accumulating a batch may also be considered. For example, a batch may be defined as the number of projects accumulated over some budget period, such as a year. Alternatively, a batch might be defined in terms of a specific number of proposals that constitute a sufficient backlog to justify the effort of allocating funds among them.

We have generally assumed that the firm has a fixed budget that it wishes to allocate to the proposals, or, in a decentralized case, to the divisions themselves. This may occur in the firm that decides to limit its capital budget to the sum of depreciation charges plus retained earnings in the current period, or in the firm that makes an estimate of the internally and externally available funds that it can, or is willing to, obtain in the current period. This does not explicitly allow the size of the capital budget to depend on the number and nature of the projects discovered. Thus it does not consider explicitly the case in which management's attitude is, "Show us a good proposal and somehow we will raise the money to fund it."

The design of capital-budgeting systems must be concerned with the co-ordination of the search and evaluation processes. These must be co-ordinated with the supply of funds available to the firm through its budgeting or decision-making arrangements. We begin to understand these delegation and co-ordination problems by looking, in the next two chapters, at the search and evaluation steps.

1. The data on capital-budgeting systems appears in such works as: Richard M. Cyert and James G. March, *A Behavorial Theory of the Firm* (Englewood Cliffs, N.J.: Prentice-Hall, 1963); Robert Eisner, *Determinants of Capital Expenditures* (Urbana: University of Illinois, Bureau of Economic and Business Research, 1956); Michael Gort, "The Planning of Investment," *Journal of Business,* Vol. XXIV, No. 1 (April, 1951); W. Warren Haynes and Martin B. Solomon, "A Misplaced Emphasis in Capital Budgeting," *Quarterly Review of Economics and Business,* Vol. II, No. 1 (February, 1962); Walter W. Heller, "The Anatomy of Investment Decisions, *Harvard Business Review,* Vol. XXIX, No. 2 (March, 1951).

2. See Chandler, *op. cit.,* pp. 114–62, and Sloan, *op. cit.,* pp. 116–48.

3. National Industrial Conference Board, *op. cit.,* pp. 21–38.

CHAPTER 4

THE SEARCH FOR OPPORTUNITIES

Co-ordination of Search

The process of searching for potential investment opportunities is costly, and the question of how much effort should be devoted to it is clearly related to the design of an effective capital-budgeting system. There is little point in carrying on an extensive program to discover opportunities if the funds available for investment are severely limited. On the other hand, if funds are available, it is important that a level of search effort be mounted consistent with making good use of these funds. Similarly, the choice of which organizational units are going to be given search tasks, and to what extent the units are free to carry out these tasks according to their own judgments, may have important consequences for the amount of search that is done, the nature of it, and the way in which the results are reported. We will be considering these design problems in subsequent sections. Our immediate purpose is to suggest some of the basic principles upon which search policy might be founded and to note the possibilities for complementarity and requirements for co-ordination that they suggest. The discussion does not deal in detail with the special problems of research and development projects, new-product opportunities, cost-reduction opportunities, and so on. Rather, it considers some generalized and highly simplified search processes that hopefully suggest the basic issues and give the discussion to follow some substance when it refers to search policy.

When a firm adopts a policy of spending, say, a fixed percentage of sales on research each year, it is a little difficult to tell what rationale offers an appropriate explanation. By seeming to let research effort depend on sales, the firm seems to say that the level of such effort is quite unrelated to marginal costs and marginal benefits. Indeed, the degree of uncertainty associated with such undertakings may be so high that any such conception is grossly unrealistic, even if the uncertainty could be explicitly considered. In such cases it is probably better that we regard a particular policy for fixing research expenditures as an experimental one. In the long run, the firm may learn if its policy is capable of improvement. Already it knows that its policy is not ridiculous or disastrous, but no rationalization is really worth attempting.

On the other hand, a policy that relates research effort to sales might have a reasonable basis. As sales grow, for example, so retained earnings may grow and thus make capital available for investment. Growing sales should thus be accompanied by growing research efforts so as to provide opportunities for the investment of these increasing funds. Likewise, growing sales in a particular product may, however crudely, be the signal that the market life of the product is now at such a point that it is time to undertake research and development on the new products that are candidates to replace it as it fades.

In considering search, one must distinguish two general situations. In some firms the stream of new investment proposals comes from the operating units without any explicit decisions as to how much effort is to be deliberately devoted to search. Proposals arise "in the natural course of business," and the firm is content to continue in this fashion. Often, the number of such proposals regularly exceeds the ability of the firm to match them with funds. It is thus difficult for the firm to justify devoting effort to the generation of more proposals, while at the same time there may be a natural reluctance to discourage the flow of proposals for fear of missing some good opportunities. Thus the firm may tend to leave the search process undisturbed.

This situation may contain several self-regulatory features:

1. The operating divisions, which generate proposals, having some knowledge of past earnings, tend to regulate the number of proposals submitted roughly in accordance with the internal availability of capital funds.

2. If a division finds that its proposals are seldom accepted and funded (or if it has considerable difficulty learning the fate of its proposals), it may well cease to submit very many. Likewise, a division that frequently receives funds will be encouraged to submit more proposals.

3. If a division finds or suspects that an approximately fixed portion of its requests are funded, it may increase the number of requests in order to increase the funds it receives.

The second general situation arises when a deliberate effort is made to regulate the amount of resources devoted to the generation of new investment opportunities. Such efforts could vary from the establishment of a budget for the discovery and development of new product possibilities to the use of an awards system to encourage the suggestion of cost-reduction possibilities. It is this deliberate consideration of search policy that is discussed below.

In looking at the search process, we suppress for the present the evaluation step. We assume that search implies some evaluation and that the budgeting decision may be made at any time after the search process has produced a proposal. In the next chapter the integration of search and evaluation will be considered. The present analysis may be read as though the costs of search also included the costs of whatever evaluation effort is devoted to the projects discovered.

Basic Problems in Search Policy

We will be concerned here with the question of how much effort should be devoted to searching out investment opportunities. The questions of how one discovers opportunities for investments in new products, new capacity, cost-reduction projects, or replacement projects are not specifically considered. One may imagine that a firm can control search effort in two basic ways. It may decide in advance how much effort will be devoted to search during a budget period. This decision might be expressed by:

1. Determining the number or dollar value of projects that will be discovered during the period and thus committing the firm to whatever expenditures are required to do this. Since the cost of discovering a project is generally subject to considerable uncertainty, the total cost of such a program will be a matter of uncertainty as well.

2. Determining the total resources to be expended or level of search effort to be maintained during the period. In this case the expenditures are determined, but the number and dollar volume of projects produced are matters of uncertainty.

Where the firm must make such commitments in advance of the budget period, it may be thought of as basing its policy on explicit or implicit estimates of the expected costs of search and the expected gains therefrom. Generally speaking, it would attempt to plan its efforts so that the marginal cost of search effort is made equal to the marginal gain. This decision clearly involves considerable uncertainty and can be understood only in terms of averages or expected values. This prior determination of search policy appears in several examples in Chapter VI. Clearly, the amount of search effort planned will be a function of the funds available to the firm. If search policy is delegated to the divisions, then they may be expected to determine it in relation to the investment funds made available to them.

A second basic mode of control for search effort is the dynamic or sequential one. In this case after each project is discovered, the question of stopping or continuing search is examined in the light of the proposals presently available. The marginal cost of continuing search is compared with the marginal gain from doing so, and the decision made accordingly. Again, of course, these quantities are matters of considerable uncertainty and can be thought of only in an expected value sense. This dynamic mode of control is more complex, yet potentially more profitable, than advance determination of search effort.

Dynamic Search Policies

The uncertainty associated with the costs and results of the search process may make it difficult to employ precise calculations in the formulation of search policy. Yet such policies must be made either explicitly or implicitly, with whatever precision may be obtained through cumulating information and experience. The point of this discussion is to suggest some possible logical bases for search policy and the sort of information that would be required to apply the resulting policies. In this way one can say something of the consequences of centralizing or decentralizing decisions about search in the face of various patterns of information distribution throughout the organization.

For simplicity we will assume that the cost of searching for and discovering an investment proposal is viewed by the policy-maker as a random variable, and that the distribution of this variable does not change as search progresses. In actuality the process of search produces information about its costs, and thus one would expect the estimates of cost to be revised as search progresses. It would seem, however, that no serious difficulties could be encountered in adding the impact of this information to the analysis that follows. Similarly, the results of search are regarded as uncertain, and the present worth of an investment opportunity that has not been discovered is taken to be a random variable. Here, as well, knowledge may be accumulated as search progresses, and one's view of the opportunity environment may be sequentially revised in the light of this knowledge. Though this has not specifically been reflected in the logic developed, it might be added without great difficulty.

Acceptability and Search

We begin with a basic hypothesis that suggests a number of insights into the question of investing in projects already discovered or searching for additional ones. This hypothesis, advanced by Simon and March,[1] says: "Most human decision-making, whether organizational or individual, is concerned with the discovery and selection of satisfactory alternatives; only in exceptional cases is it concerned with the discovery and selection of optimal alternatives." An optimal alternative is one that is demonstrably the best of all possible alternatives. To discover an optimal alternative, it is necessary to first search out all of the possible alternatives and then apply a principle of choice that will lead to a preferred course of action. A satisfactory alternative is one that simply meets some minimum standards of acceptability. To find an acceptable alternative, it is not generally necessary to search out all possible alternatives. The validity of this hypothesis can be roughly checked by immediate reference to experience. Many jobs are filled not by literally searching out the very best man but by finding one who has the qualifications necessary to do the job. Many investments are made not by searching out the opportunity that will literally yield the greatest return but by taking advantage of opportunities that will yield a 10 per cent return and rejecting those yielding less than this rate.

This hypothesis, applied to the problem of searching or not searching for additional alternatives, suggests that if among the alternatives presently under consideration there are one or more satisfactory alternatives, no further search will be made. If the alternatives under consideration are not satisfactory, a search may be pursued until a satisfactory alternative is discovered.

The way in which this principle is applied is determined by the process of selecting a standard of acceptability. This standard is often called an aspiration level. Ideally, the aspiration level should be set so that it terminates search at the point where the expected marginal cost of continuing search is equal to the expected marginal gain. Some examples of such aspiration levels, which might be called optimal aspiration levels, are indicated below. On the other hand, the aspiration level might be established on other grounds and, from the point of view of search costs and benefits, appear quite arbitrary. This may include, of course, aspiration levels set on the basis of incomplete knowledge of available funds, projects so far discovered, search costs, or the character of the opportunity environment.

We can illustrate basic principles most simply by supposing that the firm searches in an opportunity environment in which all projects require approximately the same initial investment and that the firm wishes to invest in one such project. Later, we shall consider how this assumption may be relaxed.

We begin with the case in which search is not limited by time or other resources to some maximum number of opportunities. Rather, search may be extended until a project is discovered that meets an optimal aspiration level requirement.

Transitory Opportunities

Let P = the present worth of the project; $f(P)$ = the probability distribution of P that describes the opportunity environment in which search is being carried on (that is, we regard the present worth of an as yet undiscovered project as a random variable P, with probability distribution of $f(P)$); and A = an aspiration level (expressed in dollars).

We consider the act of searching for and discovering an investment opportunity as a "trial." For a given aspiration level A, the probability of discovering an opportunity with present worth greater than or equal to A on a given trial is

$$p = \int_{P=A}^{\infty} f(P)dP \, .$$

The probability of $n - 1$ trials prior to the first discovery of such a project is

$$p(1 - p)^{n-1}$$

and the expected number of trials required to find the first project that has present worth meeting the aspiration level requirement is

$$E(n) = \sum_{n=1}^{\infty} np(1 - p)^{n-1} = \frac{1}{p} \, .$$

Given that the aspiration level requirement is met, the expected present worth is

$$E(A) = \frac{\int_{A}^{\infty} Pf(P)dP}{\int_{A}^{\infty} f(P)dP}$$

$$E(A) = \frac{1}{p} \int_{A}^{\infty} Pf(P)dP \, .$$

If c is the unit cost of search—that is, the cost of a trial—the expected net present worth as a function of A is

$$E(A) = \frac{1}{p} \int_A^\infty Pf(P)dP - \frac{c}{p} = \frac{1}{p}\left\{ \int_A^\infty Pf(P)dP - c \right\}.$$

Taking the first derivative of this with respect to A, we have

$$\frac{dE(A)}{dA} = \frac{1}{p^2}\left\{ p(-Af(A)) + f(A)\left[\int_A^\infty Pf(P)dP - c \right] \right\}.$$

Setting this derivative equal to 0 and assuming $f(A) \neq 0$, we have

$$-A_0 p + \int_{A_0}^\infty Pf(P)dP - c = 0.$$

Thus the optimal value A_0 is the solution to this equation. Note that this may be written as

$$\int_{A_0}^\infty (P - A_0)f(P)dP = c$$

a form that will be of further interest.

Note also that this may be interpreted as setting the expected increase in present worth above the aspiration level equal to the cost of obtaining this increase.

To illustrate, suppose that the present worth of a project is regarded as a uniformly distributed random variable over the range

$$a \leq P \leq b.$$

The expression

$$\int_{A_0}^b (P - A_0)f(P)dP = c$$

may be written

$$\frac{(b + A_0)(b - A_0)}{2(b - a)} - \frac{A_0(b - A_0)}{b - a} = c.$$

Solving and selecting the appropriate root yields

$$A_0 = b - \sqrt{2c(b-a)}.$$

Persistent Opportunities

Suppose that some search has been conducted and that the best of the opportunities discovered so far has present worth P_0. Suppose search is to be continued until a better opportunity is found. The expected gain from such a policy, considered as a function of P_0 is

$$E(P_0) = \frac{1}{\displaystyle\int_{P_0}^{\infty} f(P)dP} \left\{ \int_{P_0}^{\infty} Pf(P)dP - c \right\} - P_0.$$

$E(P_0) = 0$ implies

$$\int_{P_0}^{\infty} Pf(P)dP - c - P_0 \int_{P_0}^{\infty} f(P)dP = 0$$

or

$$\int_{P_0}^{\infty} (P - P_0)f(P)dP - c = 0.$$

Now if we stop search when the gain is no longer positive, this is equivalent to stopping when the present worth of the best available opportunity is greater than or equal to A_0, the optimal aspiration level in the case of transitory opportunities. Thus we can say that whether the opportunities are persistent or transitory, one should stop search when the best available opportunity (which may be the only available opportunity) has present worth greater than or equal to A_0. Note also that this is equivalent to stopping when the marginal cost of one more trial c is just equal to the expected marginal gain from one more trial:

$$\int_{P_0}^{\infty} (P - P_0)f(P)dP.$$

Note that if search is unlimited, the value of $E(P_0)$ is the same whether opportunities are persistent or transitory.

Limited Search, Persistent Opportunities

Suppose search is limited to the discovery of at most one more opportunity and that the best available opportunity has present worth P_0. The expected gain from continuing search is

$$E_1(P_0) = \int_{P_0}^{\infty} (P - P_0)f(P)dP - c .$$

If one decides to continue if $E_1(P_0) > 0$, and stop otherwise, the policy is the same as that derived before; that is, stop if $P_0 > A_0$; otherwise, continue.

Note, however, that the expected gain when opportunities are persistent, $E_1(P_0)$, is greater than the expected gain when opportunities are transitory. For the transitory case, the expected gain is

$$\int_{P=0}^{\infty} Pf(P)dP - c - P_0 = \int_{P=P_0}^{\infty} (P - P_0)f(P)dP - c$$

$$- \int_{P=0}^{\infty} (P_0 - P)f(P)dP = E_1(P_0) - \int_{P=0}^{P_0} (P_0 - P)f(P)dP.$$

Suppose now that search is limited to at most two more trials. If one more trial is carried out, the problem then becomes what to do when one more trial remains, as discussed above. Thus if $P_0 > A_0$, we know that the second trial will not be carried out.

In this case, $E_2(P_0) =$ the expected gain when search is limited to, at most, two more trials and when the best available opportunity has present worth P_0, and

$$E_2(P_0) = \int_{P_1=P_0}^{\infty} (P_1 - P_0)f(P_1)dP_1 - c$$

where P_1 is the present worth of the opportunity discovered on the first trial. Since we know that $E_2(P_0)$ will be positive only if $P_0 < A_0$, and since by our original assumption $P_0 > A_0$, once again the same rule would apply; that is, stop if $P_0 > A_0$, otherwise, continue. Further, this rule could be shown by induction to hold (under the original assumption that $P_0 > A_0$) for all values of n, the maximum number of additional trials.

Consider now the case of $P_0 < A_0$ and search limited to at most two more trials. For this case

$$E_2(P_0) = \int\limits_{P_1 = A_0}^{\infty} (P_1 - P_0)f(P_1)dP_1 - c + E_1(P_0) \int\limits_{P_1 = 0}^{P_0} f(P_1)dP_1$$

$$+ \int\limits_{P_1 = P_0}^{A_0} \{E_1(P_1) + P_1 - P_0\}f(P_1)dP_1 .$$

If $P_0 = A_0$, the above expression for $E_2(P_0)$ becomes zero, while if $P_0 < A_0$, the above expression will be positive. Thus again the best policy would be to stop if $P_0 < A_0$; otherwise, continue. Again by induction it may be seen that this result holds for all values of n, thus establishing the result that the optimal policy for persistent opportunities is the same whether or not search is limited.

Note that $E_1(P_0) \leq E_2(P_0)$ and in general $E_{n-1}(P_0) \leq E_n(P_0)$. As n grows very large, the result for limited search should approach that for unlimited search. To see that this happens, assume that for large n

$$E_n(P_0) = E_{n-1}(P_0) .$$

If $P_0 > A_0$, we would cease search immediately; thus

$$E_n(P_0) = P_0 = E_{n-1}(P_0)$$

which is the same result as for unlimited research search. If $P_0 < A_0$, we would continue. The expected gain from continuing is

$$E_n(P_0) = \int\limits_{A_0}^{\infty} (P_1 - P_0)f(P_1)dP_1 - c + E_{n-1}(P_0) \int\limits_{P_1 = 0}^{P_0} f(P_1)dP_1$$

$$+ \int\limits_{P_1 = P_0}^{A_0} \{E_{n-1}(P_1) + P_1 - P_0\}f(P_1)dP_1 .$$

By previous assumption, $E_n(P_0) = E_{n-1}(P_0)$ for large n. Assume the hypothesis

$$E_{n-1}(P_1) = E_n(P_1) = \cfrac{1}{\int\limits_{P = A_0}^{\infty} f(P)dP} \left\{ \int\limits_{P = A_0}^{\infty} (P - P_1)f(P)dP - c \right\}$$

to be true. That is, assume for the large n the expectation is the same for limited as for unlimited search. It would follow that

$$E_{n-1}(P_1) = E_n(P_1) = E_n(P_0) + P_0 - P_1.$$

$E_n(P_0)$ then becomes with these substitutions

$$E_n(P_0) = \int_{P_1=A_0}^{\infty} (P_1 - P_0)f(P_1)\,dP_1 + E_n(P_0)\int_{P_1=0}^{P_0} f(P_1)\,dP_1 + \int_{P_1=P_0}^{A_0} E_n(P_0)f(P_1)\,dP_1 - c$$

$$= \frac{1}{\displaystyle\int_{P_1=A_0}^{\infty} f(P_1)\,dP_1} \left\{ \int_{P_1=A_0}^{\infty} (P_1 - P_0)f(P_1)\,dP_1 - c \right\}.$$

Thus the hypothesis is confirmed.

Limited Search, Transitory Opportunities

Suppose now that search is limited to at most n more opportunities and that these opportunities are transitory. Suppose an opportunity with present worth P_0 has just been discovered and one more opportunity remains. If we pass over the opportunity presently being considered, we will have to accept the next (and last) one discovered. The expected present worth resulting from this is given by

$$e_n = \int_{P=0}^{\infty} Pf(P)\,dP - c.$$

We would prefer to continue if

$$P_0 < e_n.$$

Otherwise, it would be best to choose the opportunity presently being considered. Let A_{n-1} be the value of P_0, which satisfies the expression

$$P_0 = e_n.$$

One may then formulate the policy. If we arrive at the $n-1$st opportunity (and one has not been previously accepted), we will accept the $n-1$st project if its present worth is greater than A_{n-1}; otherwise, we will continue.

Suppose next that an opportunity is under consideration, and at most two more may be discovered. As before, let the present worth of the opportunity being considered be P_0. If we do not accept it, we will discover a subsequent opportunity and be faced with the problem already solved. That is, if the present worth of the subsequently discovered opportunity is greater than A_{n-1}, we will accept it; otherwise, we will continue. Thus the expected present worth of continuing with at most two more opportunities remaining may be written as

$$\int_{P=A_{n-1}}^{\infty} P f(P) dP - c + e_n \int_{P=0}^{A_{n-1}} f(P) dP = e_{n-1} + e_n \int_{P=0}^{A_{n-1}} f(P) dP \, .$$

The currently considered opportunity will be accepted if

$$P_0 \geq e_{n-1} + e_n \int_{P=0}^{A_{n-1}} f(P) dP \, .$$

Otherwise, we will continue. Let A_{n-2} be the value of P_0 for which equality holds in the above expression. Then, as before, we will accept or pass according to whether P_0 is greater than A_{n-2}. The form of this policy may be immediately generalized so that the aspiration level for the situation in which at most k opportunities remain to be discovered is given by

$$A_{n-k} = \sum_{j=k+1}^{n} (e_j - c) \prod_{i=k+1}^{j-1} \left\{ \int_{P=0}^{A_i} f(P) dP \right\} \, .$$

As one would expect, the fewer the opportunities remaining to be discovered, the lower the aspiration level. That is, as search resources become more nearly exhausted, one becomes willing to accept projects of progressively lower present worth. On the other hand, if the number of opportunities remaining grows very large, the resulting aspiration level approaches that found in the case of unlimited search.[2]

Random Search Limitations

We may generalize directly to the case in which the limitation on search is not certainly known. That is, search is limited to at most n more opportunities where n is taken to be a random variable. If we assume that once the process of search for an opportunity is begun, it may be completed when no changes need be made in the policies for persistent opportunities.

Here it was shown that the aspiration level would be the same whether or not search was limited, and thus a random limitation on search will have no effect. In the case of transitory opportunities, it is necessary to introduce the probability distribution of the number of remaining opportunities that may be sought.

Total Budget and Project Size Assumptions

So far, it has been assumed that all projects require the same initial investment and that the budget available is sufficient to fund exactly one project. Suppose now we continue the assumption of fixed project size but that funds are available to invest in several projects. We may then think of the budget as having a fixed number of "positions" to be filled with projects. In the case of unlimited search in an environment of persistent opportunities, the analysis developed may be applied to each budget position. That is, one searches for projects to fill a given budget position until one is obtained that meets the aspiration level. The process is then repeated for another budget position, and so on until all the positions are filled. In the case of unlimited search in an environment of transitory opportunities, the same procedure may be used.

In the case of limited search for persistent opportunities, one might operate as follows. Find for a budget of B positions, the first B opportunities that can be discovered and rank them. Apply the principle developed for $B = 1$ to the worst opportunity currently in the budget. Repeat this process until search effort is exhausted or no longer justified by the marginal cost–marginal gain principle. For limited search in an environment of transitory opportunities, the principles are similar but somewhat more complex to state. Suppose at any stage in the process of filling a budget of B positions there are m positions remaining to be filled. An opportunity just discovered is under consideration, and limitations on search permit the discovery of, at most, n more opportunities. At this point one must choose between

1. Taking the opportunity currently under consideration and proceeding with the problem of filling $m - 1$ positions with a search process limited to at most n additional opportunities, and

2. Passing over the opportunity currently under consideration and proceeding with the problem of filling m positions with a search process limited to at most n additional opportunities.

One might compute the expected present worth for each of these two actions and choose accordingly. The result would be an aspiration level value for the project under consideration that would be a function of m and n.

Consider next the assumption of fixed project size. To relax this assumption completely might be to assume that an investment opportunity may be undertaken on any scale whatsoever. That is, one has complete freedom to select the size of the initial investment to be made. The firm that wishes, as we have assumed, to maximize the expected present worth of its investments will wish to consider the investment of all available funds in each opportunity discovered. Thus the problem reduces to that discussed originally.

If the opportunity environment consists of projects of varying sizes, the situation becomes markedly more complex. One would require the probability distribution of project sizes as well as the probability distribution of present worths. It would appear, however, that the differences in results would be differences in detail and not in principle.

Centralized and Decentralized Systems

The problems of search discussed here represent but one aspect of the design of capital-budgeting systems. Good designs will seek some compatibility among:

Search policy

Evaluation policy

Delegation patterns

Budgeting policy (continuous, batch, etc.)

Available funds

In a highly centralized system all budgeting might be done at headquarters and a search policy designed with consideration given to headquarters' knowledge of:

Available funds

Divisional search costs

Divisional opportunity environments

Projects discovered to date

If the headquarters unit did indeed have good knowledge of these factors, a policy could be established that might achieve a considerable effectiveness for the firm.

A highly decentralized system might involve allocating a budget to the divisions and permitting each division to design its own search policy based upon its knowledge of its own search costs, opportunity environment, and portfolio of projects so far discovered. The division could then move toward optimizing this policy relative to its own operation and budget. Whether the budget allocation made by headquarters was good would be an important question here. Generally, one would expect such a decentralized system to perform less well than the centralized one suggested above, given equivalent knowledge about such things as search costs and opportunity environments in each case.

In between these two designs are a multitude of possible systems in which search policy is determined to a greater or lesser degree in a centralized fashion.

1. March and Simon, *op. cit.,* pp. 136–42.

2. For a more elegant mathematical statement of some of the problems of search, see James B. McQueen, "Optimal Policies for a Class of Search and Evaluation Problems, *"Management Science,* Vol. X, No. 4 (July, 1964), 746–59.

5

CHAPTER

EVALUATION

Bayes Models for Evaluation Policy

We have used the term "search" to describe the process by which possible capital-investment opportunities are discovered or identified. We have supposed that the search process produces opportunities that are described in terms of some preliminary or basic information. For example, we would think of the search for possible machines to carry out a particular step in the production process as resulting in a list of several machines described by manufacturers, approximate price range, and rough statements of technological capabilities. From this point on, the process of obtaining additional detailed information and verifying that already in hand is undertaken, in preparation for the actual decision step. This data-gathering process we will call evaluation of the possibilities. It is basically a process aimed at reducing the uncertainty in the decision to be made. In this section we will examine a basic model of the process of evaluation and then consider the possible consequences of carrying on the process at various places within an organization. The model is essentially an application of Bayesian concepts and draws directly on the ideas in statistical decision theory. The importance of these ideas for management-decision problems is due largely to the work of Schlaifer.[1]

For purposes of this discussion, Bayesian analysis may be thought of as contributing two main ideas:

1. A decision-maker's uncertainty about future events is expressed by thinking of these events as random phenomena. Thus the language of probability theory becomes the language for expressing uncertainty. (Most of us were brought up to think that probabilities referred only to relative frequencies in repeated experiments.) It is not suggested that probability is the "natural" language managers use to express uncertainty. Indeed, it must be learned, and what concerns us is whether the benefits would support the trouble of learning it.

2. Probability theory also provides a logic suggesting how this expression will be modified as a result of receiving additional information. If one accepts this logical guide to the evaluation of data, one of the exciting possibilities is that the process of blending mature, expert judgment with data may be studied and perhaps even delegated. After all, one major reason the headquarters group makes the big decisions is that they have the most experience and can make the best judgments.

These ideas hold promise for overcoming a number of the difficulties resulting from the suppression of risk. To illustrate, consider the problems of planning the firm's information-gathering activities. Are we now ready to make a final decision about a particular investment proposal, or should we have the staff get more data first? Obviously, such questions must be answered once risk creeps into the capital-budgeting process; yet they have not received much attention because they, too, fall victim to the phenomenon of risk suppression. The possibility of treating them somewhat more explicitly brings them to light.

As an example of these questions, consider the manager who is faced with the classical problem of choosing among mutually exclusive investment proposals.

1. Should he accept one of the proposals immediately on the basis of his experience and the evidence now in hand?

2. If not, how much should be spent on getting further information on each of the proposals? Some proposals will be well supported and characterized by low uncertainty. Money will not be spent on these. Others will appear more uncertain; yet if they are obviously good or obviously bad proposals, little money need be spent to further establish this.

3. Answering question 2 implies knowing something about how data-gathering effort would be employed if it was to be expended

on a given proposal. Should one get more data on the near-term cash flows or those further in the future? (The latter are traditionally the most uncertain.) Should one try to make better predictions of service life or the rate of technological obsolescence?

4. One can ask both: (a) What is the optimal amount of money for the manager to spend, and how should it be allocated?, and (b) If the manager has only a limited amount of money (or time) to devote to evaluation, how should it be allocated?

Evaluation Policies in Practice

In discussing highly refined policies for the evaluation of projects, it is perhaps wise to keep in mind certain difficulties that may be associated with the implementation of those policies. For example:

1. Evaluation may tend to be a "lumpy" process in that it is more economical to undertake a single evaluation effort for a given project than to conduct an evaluation based on a sequential policy. There may be important set-up costs that dictate that the amount of evaluation should be decided in advance and accomplished in one effort. This may preclude policies in which the amount of evaluation depends on what is known about the project in question or what is known about other projects subsequently studied.

2. There may be costs that dictate that evaluation of a project must be carried out essentially at the time the project is discovered.

3. The cost of information is difficult to estimate because in many instances it is highly non-linear and sometimes has value for more than one project being considered by the firm. Indeed, the firm may search for projects that can utilize information already available.

The models with which we deal here are rich models and as such require rather rich input data. One can well ask if such data is, or could be, available at a cost reasonable enough to make the analysis useful. This is a difficult question to answer, and perhaps the present discussion should be considered a preliminary step in answering a slightly different question: "If the necessary input data were routinely available, of what consequence would this be?" That is, the analysis might be viewed as a step in considering what justification might be given for making the necessary input data available. Clearly, it would be surprising to find it currently available on a routine basis in explicit form in many firms. Yet to the extent that the analysis does reflect what is going on, one may infer that the necessary data, or something like it, is available at least in implicit form.

Some basic distinctions may be recalled before considering the various problems of evaluation that follow. The situation implied by the term *ample funds* is the situation in which the firm finds itself with more capital available than investment projects it is willing to consider. This is roughly the situation in those companies having large pools of capital invested in government bonds or some such "near cash" asset. In some cases such funds are clearly set aside for some future project such as a major acquisition, but in others at least a portion of these funds is available for current investments of the sort we are studying. The opposite situation is referred to as the *ample projects* situation. Here the firm is ordinarily confronted with more projects than it has funds to undertake. We are thus considering the firm that sets an upper limit on the funds to be invested and finds that it must budget these funds by choosing only some of the projects available. It may, for example, limit its investment in any one year to an amount equal to the sum of depreciation charged plus earnings retained for that year.

Evaluation policies may be classified as static or dynamic according to the following conceptions. If the decision as to how much evaluation effort will be devoted to a project depends only on the characteristics of the project itself, evaluation is called static. Thus an experiment of fixed sample size or a sequential experiment might be conducted in evaluation of the project; and as long as the design of these experiments did not require knowledge of other projects, the policy would be considered a static one. If, on the other hand, the amount of evaluation effort expended on a project depends on the previous discovery and evaluation of other projects, the evaluation policy will be called dynamic. For example, if a number of very good projects has already been discovered and evaluated, and if these projects would more than utilize the available funds, the firm may reduce the amount of evaluative effort expended on projects subsequently discovered.[2]

Ample Funds *

To illustrate how these problems may be approached, consider a project that has been discovered and is to be evaluated. Suppose that ample funds are available and the decision to invest or not invest depends simply on whether the final estimate of the project's present worth after evaluation is positive or negative. If perfect information was available, the present worth of the project P would be computed according to the relation

$$P = \sum_{t=0}^{N} a^t R_t$$

* The starred sections are primarily expository and may be omitted by readers familiar with, or uninterested in, the details of Bayesian analysis.

where $R_t = $ the net cash flow at time t ; $a = $ the present worth factor $1/1 + i$; and $N = $ the duration of the project.

We shall suppose that under even the most favorable conditions of knowledge attainable, the decision-maker would regard the R_t as random variables. For simplicity we shall consider the special case in which the R_t are viewed as independent normally distributed random variables, with means $\overline{R}_t$ and with variances $\sigma^2{}_t$.

The expected value of the present worth of the project is then

$$\overline{P} = \sum_{t=0}^{N} a^t \overline{R}_t .$$

In order to deal with a specific problem, we shall suppose that the values of the $\sigma^2{}_t$ are known, but that the decision-maker is uncertain about the means $\overline{R}_t$.[3] This may be interpreted as saying that, prior to actually undertaking the project, even if all conceivable information were obtained, the cash flow at the end of period t would be regarded as a random variable with mean $\overline{R}_t$ and variance $\sigma^2{}_t$. One simply cannot find out in advance exactly what the value of R_t will be. Further, although for purposes of illustration we will assume that the variances are known, the means are only imperfectly or uncertainly known by the decision-maker. He is therefore interested in considering possible programs of data collection that will reduce his uncertainty (give him better knowledge) as to the means $\overline{R}_t$.

His uncertainty about the $\overline{R}_t$ is expressed by regarding them as random variables that are independently normally distributed with means m'_t and variances $\sigma'^2{}_t$. These distributions are called the prior distributions of the $\overline{R}_t$ to indicate that they express the knowledge of the decision-maker about the $\overline{R}_t$ prior to undertaking any program of data collection.[4]

Based on these prior distributions and the assumption of independence among them, we can write the prior distribution of the expected or mean present worth of the project. It will be a normally distributed random variable with mean given by

$$M' = \sum_{t=0}^{N} a^t m'_t$$

and variance given by

$$V' = \sum_{t=0}^{N} a^{2t} \sigma_t'^2 .$$

To reduce uncertainty about the mean cash flows, various sorts of observation programs might be undertaken. For example:

1. Data might be obtained on the cash flows from similar projects the decision-maker regards as coming from the same population as the project under study.

2. Since the cash flow in any period is the sum of a number of components of income and expense, data might be obtained on these individual components from situations regarded as being from the same population as the project under study.

3. Instead of observing cash flows or their components directly, one might obtain indirect evidence known to be correlated with the cash flows. For example, if the revenue from a certain project is felt to be correlated with the level of disposable personal income, the data on the latter quantity might be obtained. This in turn might be used to project disposable personal income to the time periods anticipated in the project, and the correlation used to produce a projection of cash flows.

Whatever the data obtained, the Bayesian evaluation process requires that one be able to state its likelihood. That is, it is necessary to be able to give, for any data y, the probability of y conditional on a particular value of $\bar{R}_t$, say $f(y|\bar{R}_t)$. In other words, one needs to know the likelihood of the sample on the assumption that a particular hypothesis about $\bar{R}_t$ is true. If, for example, one observes the cash flow in a particular period t for another project believed to be of the same statistical population as the project under study, then this observation, say R_t, may be regarded as a normally distributed random variable with mean $\bar{R}_t$ and variance σ^2_t. We would then write

$$f(R_t|\bar{R}_t) = N(\bar{R}_t, \sigma_t^2).$$

If a sample of size n of such observations is obtained, then

$$f(m|\bar{R}_t) = N\left(R_t, \frac{\sigma_t^2}{n}\right)$$

where m is the mean of the n observations.

If a component of a cash flow is observed, the required likelihood is conditional on various hypotheses about the component. For example, if we take a particular cost C_t as the subject for study, we may consider the mean cash flow to be

$$R_t = \bar{I}_t - \bar{C}_t.$$

Given prior probability distributions for $\bar{I}_t$ and $\bar{C}_t$ and perhaps the assumption that these two random variables are independent, we can write the prior probability distribution of $\bar{R}_t$. When an observation C_t is obtained, we will require the likelihood of C_t conditional on $\bar{C}_t$, or $f(C_t|\bar{C}_t)$.

Given the necessary likelihood function, the data may be used to transform the prior probability distributions into posterior probability distribution using the logic of Bayes's theorem. As an illustration, we consider the case in which a sample of observations of R_t are obtained. The effect of these observations is to transform the normal prior distribution of $\bar{R}_t$ into a posterior distribution that is also normal. The following expository section informally establishes this result.

The Normal Prior–Normal Posterior Relation *

Consider a random process whose output is a sequence of independent normally distributed random variables, x. Suppose that the standard deviation of x is known, but the mean is not. Uncertainty about the mean is expressed by regarding it as a random variable. This distribution of the mean is called the prior, and we will consider the case in which it is normal.

Let

$$f'(u) = \text{the prior distribution of } u$$

where

$m' = $ the prior mean of u

$\sigma' = $ the prior standard deviation of u (the better our knowledge of the process mean, the smaller σ').

We define for later use:

$$n' = \frac{\sigma^2}{\sigma'^2}$$

Suppose now that a sample of observations of the output of the process is obtained and represented by $x_1, x_2, \ldots, x_n$.

Let $f''(u) = $ the posterior distribution of u. Using Bayes's theorem to find the posterior distribution, we obtain

$$f''(u|m) = \frac{f(m|u)f'(u)}{\int f(m|u)f'(u)du}.$$

Substitution and simplification yield

$$f''(u|m) = \frac{1}{\sqrt{2\pi}\sigma/\sqrt{n'+n}} e^{\dfrac{-(n'+n)\left\{u - \dfrac{n'm'+nm}{n'+n}\right\}^2}{2\sigma^2}}.$$

Thus we see that the posterior distribution is normal. In general, a normal prior distribution with sampling from a normal process leads to a normal posterior. This is called the conjugate property of the normal distribution.

To summarize, the posterior distribution of the mean in this case is normal with

$$\text{Mean} = \frac{n'm' + nm}{n' + n}$$

$$\text{Variance} = \frac{\sigma^2}{n' + n}$$

Note that the posterior mean is the weighted average of the prior mean and the sample mean, the weights being n' and the sample size respectively. The weight n' is inversely proportional to the prior variance of the mean and reflects the prior evidence or information the decision-maker has. If the prior variance is small (the decision-maker has good information), n' will be large, and considerable weight will be attached to the prior mean. If the prior variance is large (the decision-maker is very uncertain), n' will be small, and most of the weight will be given to the sample data.

As n grows large, the relative importance of the prior information declines. As n grows small, the relative importance of the prior information increases.

Sufficiency *

An interesting point for the design of management information systems is that the individual values of the sample observations were not used, but the information they contained was summarized by the sample mean. The sample mean in this case is known as a sufficient statistic, meaning that we lose no information when we summarize the observations in their mean. The sense in which this is true is roughly indicated by the following example.

Consider a normal process with mean $= u$ and Var $= \sigma^2$. Suppose that σ^2 is known, but u is regarded as a random variable with prior distribution given by $f'(u) = N(m', \sigma'^2)$. Suppose now an experiment is performed that yields two observations, x_1 and x_2. Consider two ways in which this experiment might be reported: Report 1 consists of the sample values x_1 and x_2; report 2 consists only of the mean m of the two sample values. We shall say that the reports are equivalent if the posterior variance of the sample mean is the same, no matter which report is given. If these two reports are equivalent, one contains all the useful information contained in the other. (Information is useful to the extent it reduces the posterior variance.)

If report 2 contains all the information in report 1, then we shall say that m is a sufficient report or a sufficient statistic. Consider report 1 first, and suppose that the value of x_1 is obtained. As a result, the posterior variance of u will be

$$\frac{\sigma^2}{n'+1} = \frac{\sigma^2}{\sigma^2/\sigma'^2 + 1}$$

Consider now this posterior variance to be a prior variance, and suppose that the value x_2 is obtained. The posterior variance then becomes

$$\frac{\sigma^2}{n'+2}.$$

Now consider report 2. We can think of the original normal process as one that generates m's. It is known that the variance of m (for samples of size 2) is given by $\sigma^2/2$. The posterior variance of u may then be expressed as

$$\frac{\sigma^2/2}{\dfrac{\sigma^2/2}{\sigma'^2} + 1} = \frac{\sigma^2}{n'+2}.$$

The posterior variance is, therefore, the same for report 2 as for report 1, and m is a sufficient statistic for the observations x_1 and x_2. The important point here is that one must be careful in summarizing data not to lose information in the process. The relevance of this to the problem of evaluation is suggested by the following example.

Consider two modes of observation:

1. Observe the present worth of a project considered to be from the same population as the project under study.

2. Observe the cash flows from situations considered to be the same statistically as those for the project under study; that is, observe N values, $R_1, \ldots, R_n$. We continue the assumption that these are independent random variables.

Are these two modes of observation equivalent in the sense of their conveying the same amount of information? Put another way, can one summarize the N values $R_1, \ldots, R_n$ by computing

$$P = \sum_{t=0}^{N} a^t R_t$$

without loss of information?

To demonstrate that the answer to these questions is in the negative, we consider a situation in which $N = 1$ and $a = 1$. The prior mean of P is

$$M' = m'_0 + m'_1.$$

Assume the prior distributions of the R_t to be normal with means m'_t and variances σ'^2_t, and that the prior distribution of $\bar{P}$ is normal with mean M' and variance V'. Now let

$$n'_t = \frac{\sigma_t^2}{\sigma_t'^2}$$

$$n' = \frac{\sigma_0^2 + \sigma_1^2}{\sigma_0'^2 + \sigma_1'^2}$$

M'' = the posterior mean of $\bar{P}$
V'' = the posterior variance of $\bar{P}$.

The basic question is, then, Is a report of P equivalent to a report of R_0 and R_1?

If P is reported,

$$M'' = \frac{n'M' + P}{n' + 1}$$

$$V'' = \frac{\sigma_0^2 + \sigma_1^2}{n' + 1}$$

If R_0 and R_1 are reported,

$$M'' = \frac{n'_0 m'_0 + R_0}{n'_0 + 1} + \frac{n'_1 m'_1 + R_1}{n'_1 + 1}$$

$$V'' = \frac{\sigma_0^2}{n'_0 + 1} + \frac{\sigma_1^2}{n'_1 + 1}$$

If these two reports are equivalent, M'' and V'' should be independent of the report given. If $n' = n'_0 + n'_1$, this will be so. This reduces the problem to that illustrated above where the sample mean was shown to be sufficient, with the exception that σ_0^2 need not be equal to σ_1^2. This says roughly that if we have equally good "relative" information (as measured by n'_0 and n'_1) about R_0 and R_1, the two reports are equivalent.

Suppose, however, that the relation $n' = n'_0 = n'_1$ does not hold. We may write

$$\frac{n'M' + P}{n' + 1} = \frac{n'm'_0 + R_0}{n' + 1} + \frac{n'm'_1 + R_1}{n' + 1}$$

and ask if this can be equal to

$$\frac{n'_0 m'_0 + R_0}{n'_0 + 1} + \frac{n'_1 m'_1 + R_1}{n'_1 + 1}.$$

If $n' = n'_0 \neq n'_1$, or if $n'_0 \neq n'_1$ $\quad$ and $\quad$ $n' = n'_0$ or n'_1, clearly the two expressions above cannot be equal; if $n' \neq n'_0 \neq n'_1$, we may write

$$n' = \frac{\dfrac{n'_0(m'_0 - R_0)}{n'_0 + 1} + \dfrac{n'_1(m'_1 - R_1)}{n'_1 + 1}}{\dfrac{m'_0 - R_0}{n'_0 + 1} + \dfrac{m'_1 - R_1}{n'_1 + 1}}.$$

Thus for equality, n' would have to depend on the actual observations (which it does not), and it would not generally be true that the two reports would produce the same posterior mean for $\bar{P}$.

Given that the two reports do not contain the same information, the interesting question is, Which contains the greater amount? The intuitive answer is obviously the report of R_0 and R_1. To show that this is indeed so, we assume that the posterior variance of P is greater if the report is P than if the report is R_0 and R_1 and then show that this assumption must hold; that is

$$\frac{\sigma_0{}^2 + \sigma_1{}^2}{n' + 1} > \frac{\sigma_0{}^2}{n'_0 + 1} + \frac{\sigma_1{}^2}{n'_1 + 1}.$$

This reduces to

$$(\sigma_0 \sigma'_1 - \sigma'_0 \sigma_1)^2 > 0$$

which must be true, thus confirming the original assumption.

The following section illustrates the basic analysis involved in the economic planning of a data-collection program for the case we are discussing.

The Preposterior Analysis *

We continue to consider a normal process with known variance but uncertain mean. Our uncertainty about the mean is expressed by regarding it as a random variable with a prior distribution that is also normal.

Sample evidence will transform the prior distribution of the process mean into a posterior distribution. The posterior distribution will itself have a mean called "the posterior mean of the process mean."

Before the sample is obtained, this posterior mean must be regarded as a random variable. Thus we speak of the prior distribution of the posterior mean, and it is this distribution that we now consider.

Let $m'' =$ the mean of the posterior distribution of u. It is known that $m'' = n'm' + nm/n' + n$. Prior to taking the sample, the sample mean must be considered a random variable. It may be shown that [5]

Variance (m) = Prior Var (u) + Var $(m|u)$:

$$\frac{\sigma^2}{n'} + \frac{\sigma^2}{n} = \frac{n + n'}{n' + n} \sigma^2$$

Using this result, we can compute the prior expected value of the posterior mean:

$$E(m'') = \frac{n'm' + n(E(m) = m')}{n' + n} = m'.$$

Thus: *The prior expected value of the posterior mean is the prior mean.*

The prior variance of the posterior mean may be found as follows:

$$\text{Var } (m'') = \left\{\frac{n}{n' + n}\right\}^2 \text{Var } (m)$$

and

$$\text{Var } (m) = \frac{n}{n'(n' + n)} \sigma^2$$

Note that this may be written

$$\text{Var } (m'') = \frac{\sigma^2}{n'} - \frac{\sigma^2}{n' + n}$$

Thus we may say: As n (the sample size) grows large, the prior variance of the posterior mean will tend toward the prior variance of the mean.

To illustrate the computation of the expected value of perfect information (*EVPI*) and the expected value of sample information (*EVSI*), we will consider a simple example.

The annual profit from a project is viewed as a normally distributed random variable with known variance but uncertain mean. The decision-maker expresses his uncertainty about the mean annual profit by regarding it as a random variable with a normal distribution (the prior distribution of the mean).

His decision is whether or not to undertake the project. He uses the following decision rule: If the expected annual profit is greater than 0, undertake the project; otherwise, do not.

Prior to obtaining any information, the decision-maker examines the mean of the prior distribution of the mean annual profit. If he had to make the decision immediately, he would say:

If $m' > 0$, undertake the project.

If $m' \leq 0$, do not undertake the project.

The prior expected annual profit associated with the optimal act is thus either m' or 0.

Suppose now he is offered an opportunity to obtain perfect information about u. We shall represent this prior distribution of the posterior mean by the symbol $f(m'')$. Given perfect information, he will undertake the project with expected annual profit of m'' if $m'' > 0$, and he will not undertake the project (with expected annual profit $= 0$) if $m'' \leq 0$. Thus his expected payoff, given perfect information (but computed prior to obtaining the perfect information), is

$$\int_{m''=0}^{\infty} m'' f(m'') dm''.$$

The expected value of perfect information is thus

$$EVPI = \int_{m''=0}^{\infty} m'' f(m'') dm'' - \max(m', 0).$$

In application we shall be interested in the expected value of sample information. Suppose the decision-maker has decided in advance to take a sample of size n. We know that the prior distribution of the posterior mean is normal with:

Prior expected value of the posterior mean $= E(m'') = m'$

Prior Variance of the posterior mean $=$

$$\text{Var}(m'') = \frac{n}{n'(n'+n)} \sigma^2_* = \frac{\sigma^2}{n'} - \frac{\sigma^2}{n'+n}.$$

Again, given sample information he will undertake if $m'' > 0$; otherwise, he will not. His expected payoff, given sample information (but computed prior to obtaining the sample information), is

$$\int_{m''=0}^{\infty} m'' f(m'') dm''.$$

The expected value of sample information is

$$EVSI = \int_{m'=0}^{\infty} m'' f(m'') dm'' - \max(m', 0).$$

This would then be compared with the cost of taking a sample of size n.

This analysis immediately suggests two questions: (1) If an experiment of fixed sample size is to be done, what is the optimal value of n?, and (2) Suppose the decision-maker's problem was to choose the best of two undertakings, either or both of which could be studied by sampling experiments. How would one allocate sampling effort between the two undertakings?

Consider the case in which the cost of sampling is directly proportional to the sample size; that is, the cost of a sample size is cn. We define the expected net gain from sample information ($ENGSI$) as $ENGSI = EVSI - cn$. In the special case of $m' = 0$, this yields

$$ENGSI = \frac{\sigma}{\sqrt{2\pi}} \sqrt{\frac{n}{n'(n' + n)}} - cn.$$

The optimal sample size is then the value of n that maximizes this function.

This may be obtained by setting the first derivative of $ENGSI$ with respect to n equal to zero, and solving. This is, of course, equivalent to setting the marginal net gain equal to the marginal cost of sampling. Again, in the special case where $m' = 0$, this results in the expression

$$\sqrt{\frac{n'}{n(n' + n)}} \frac{1}{n' + n} = \frac{2\sqrt{2\pi c}}{\sigma}$$

which is to be solved for the optimal value of n.

Notice that:

1. The greater the prior expected value of the mean (m'), the smaller the $ENGSI$.

2. Since $EVSI$ approaches $EVPI$ as an upper bound, there will always be a finite optimal sample size if the cost of sampling is not zero.

3. The smaller the variance of the prior distribution (that is, the larger n'), the smaller the $ENGSI$. If the decision-maker has good information to start with, sampling information will be less valuable.

Choosing between Two Projects

Consider two projects, one of which is to be undertaken. Each project is modelled as a normal process with known standard deviation but uncertain mean.

Let

u_i = mean annual profit from project i

σ_i^2 = variance of annual profit from project i

$m_i =$ prior expected value of u_i

$\sigma_i^2/n_i =$ prior variance of u_i

$m_i'' =$ posterior mean of u_i

Suppose the projects are numbered so that $m'_1 > m'_2$. Define $d = u_2 - u_1$. The prior distribution of the posterior mean of d is normal with mean

$$\bar{d} = m'_2 - m'_1$$

$$\text{Var}\,(d) = \frac{n_1}{n'_1(n'_1 + n_1)}\,\sigma_1{}^2 + \frac{n_2}{n'_2(n'_2 + n_2)}\,\sigma_2{}^2\,.$$

The expected value of sample information will be given by

$$EVSI = \int\limits_{d=0}^{\infty} d\,N(d)$$

where $N(d) =$ prior distribution of the posterior mean of d. The problem then is to find the values of the n_i that will maximize $ENGSI$.

Allocating Investigative Effort

We now consider the problem of how investigative effort might be allocated among the R_t in evaluating a given project. The basic issue may be suggested by means of a simple example. Consider a project for which $N = 1$ and $M' = 0$. Suppose we can choose any combination of n_0 observation of R_0 and n_1 observations of R_1, and suppose these observations have unit costs of c_0 and c_1 respectively. The optimal values of n_0 and n_1 are given by the solutions of the pair of equations:

$$\frac{1}{\sqrt{2\pi}}\,\frac{d\sqrt{V^*}}{dn_0} - c_0 = 0$$

$$\frac{1}{\sqrt{2\pi}}\,\frac{d\sqrt{V^*}}{dn_1} - c_1 = 0$$

where V^* is the prior variance of the posterior mean of P.

$$V^* = \sigma^2\left\{\frac{n_0}{n'_0(n'_0 + n_0)} + \frac{a^2 n_1}{n'_1(n'_1 + n_1)}\right\}$$

The above equations yield

$$\frac{1}{(n'_0 + n_0)^2} = \frac{2\sqrt{2\pi V^* c_0}}{2}$$

$$\frac{a^2}{(n'_1 + n_1)^2} = \frac{2\sqrt{2\pi V^* c_1}}{\sigma^2}$$

Now, if we take $c_0 = c_1$, this implies

$$n_1 = a(n'_0 + n_0) - n'_1.$$

From this relation we may draw the following generalizations. The more prior information we have about a particular $\bar{R}_t$ (as measured by n'_t), the smaller the additional amount of information we shall wish to obtain. Contrarywise, if we have relatively little prior information about a particular $\bar{R}_t$, we shall be more inclined to obtain further information about it. As the interest rate increases, the value of a decreases. Thus the greater the interest rate, the greater the tendency to seek information about $\bar{R}_0$. Since one would often expect that the prior information about $\bar{R}_0$ would be more complete (smaller n'_0) than the prior information about $\bar{R}_1$, these two effects tend to offset each other.

One could, however, solve both the problem of allocating a fixed investigative budget among the $\bar{R}_t$ and the problem of finding an optimal budget combined with an optimal allocation.

In the case of ample funds, then, the optimal amount and allocation of data-collection effort can be calculated based on the prior distribution of the project present worth. In the example illustrated, it would be necessary to know the values of the $\bar{R}_t$, σ_t^2, and n'_t. If the opportunity population in which the firm (or division) was searching could be characterized by distributions for these prior parameters, one could compute in advance the expected value of the optimal data-collection (risk-reduction) expenditure for a project. This amount might simply be added to the cost of search, and the two steps in project evaluation treated as one. Further, in the case of ample funds, it is clear that evaluation based on the above optimizing principle will be much the same whether planned and carried by a division or by the headquarters group. Nothing is required in carrying out the evaluation policy other than knowledge of the prior parameters of the projects themselves.

Ample Projects and the Value of Sample Information

In considering the value of sample information, we must consider the decision problem in which the project appears. Clearly, if we are considering a project that is sure to be funded or sure not to be funded, the decision is already made, and there can be little point in gathering additional information about the project. The value of sample information is zero. In the ample funds case, one might use the decision rule that if the mean present worth is positive, the project will be funded; otherwise, it will not be funded. In this case we can compute the expected value of sample information in the usual way. If we are going to fund the best of two projects, again a method is available for computing the expected value of sample information.

The difficulty arises when we consider the evaluation of a project, the funding of which does not depend simply on the value of the posterior mean. Thus whether a project is funded may depend on the posterior means of other projects that have not yet been evaluated (or even discovered), or projects that are to be evaluated and submitted by another unit of the organization. We require then some method, necessarily approximate, for dealing with this situation.

Suppose, for example, one had more project proposals on hand than funds available to undertake them. The general strategy for evaluation would be to dispose of those projects that are clearly bad on the basis of prior information without further evaluation. Similarly, those projects that are clearly very good on the basis of prior information might be put down for funding without further evaluation. If the projects were ranked on the basis of prior information, the nearer a project to the cut-off point between those projects that would be funded if no further evaluation were made and those projects that would not be funded, the greater the expected value of sample information. These projects near the cut-off level would tend to receive most of the evaluation effort.

One approach might be to suppress differences among projects as to the amount of investment required and treat the problem as one of selecting the best N of M projects. This would require a generalization of the analysis of the best of two projects discussed previously. Instead, we shall consider a number of approximate methods that appear to have some suggestive value in connection with the ample projects case.

1. Choose a critical value for the project mean (other than zero). If the posterior mean is greater than the critical value, assume the firm will invest; otherwise, assume it will not invest. The critical value may be chosen by relating past experience on the distribution of the means of evaluated projects to the current budget amount available. This tends to reflect the fact that only *good* projects will actually be funded when there are ample projects.

2. Choose a critical value for the variance of the posterior mean. Evaluation effort is expended on each project up to the point where the variance of the posterior mean reaches this critical value. In the case of normal

prior–normal sampling, this amounts simply to choosing a value of n'' and and then sampling in amount n, where $n = n'' - n'$.

3. Evaluate projects further only if the probability of reversing the decision, given perfect information, is greater than some value p_0. Those projects that are evaluated further are subjected to either optimal sample size experiments or methods 1 or 2 above. Thus clearly good projects are considered without further evaluation, and clearly bad projects are discarded without further evaluation.

4. Assume the probability that a project will be funded is p, independent of any information about the project. The factor p is applied to the calculation of the expected value of sample information in the case of ample funds to determine a good evaluation program.

5. The probability that a project will be funded is taken to be a function of its expected present worth per dollar of investment. This probability is applied to the calculation of the expected value of sample information in the case of ample funds.

An Example

As an example of the first of these approximate policies, suppose the firm ranks projects according to the ratio of present worth to investment required. A critical or "cut-off" value of this ratio is chosen. We then assume that if a given project is found upon evaluation to have a present worth per dollar of investment greater than this critical value, it will be funded; otherwise, it will be discarded. This assumption may be valid if the firm operates on a basis of continuous budgeting. That is, as projects are discovered and evaluated, those whose ratios exceed the critical value are immediately funded, whereas others are immediately discarded. This process continues until the available funds for investment are exhausted. If, however, the firm uses batch budgeting, this assumption will be only approximately correct. Thus if the firm accumulates evaluated projects until the end of the budget period and then invests in the best of those available up to the point permitted by the available budget, some of the projects that have ratios exceeding the critical value may not be funded. On the contrary, some projects with ratios below the critical value may be funded if sufficient funds remain available.

To make such a policy explicit, let

G = the critical value of the ratio of present worth to investment

I = the investment in a particular project

$Q = IG$ = the corresponding critical value of the present worth

M' = the prior mean of P

Suppose $M' < Q$ and thus the prior choice is discard. The expected value of sample information is given by

$$EVSI = \int_{M''=Q}^{\infty} M''f(M'')dM'' - 0.$$

If $M' > Q$, the prior choice is to invest. In this case

$$EVSI = \int_{M''=Q}^{\infty} M''f(M'')dM'' - M'.$$

Thus as Q increases, $EVSI$ tends to decrease, and the amount of effort devoted to evaluation decreases as well.

If search and evaluation is performed by the divisions of the firm, the critical value of G (and thus Q for any project) may either be fixed by headquarters or established by the divisions themselves. Clearly, the results of these two methods need not be the same.

This model would be most logical if the critical value G were indeed chosen so that the probability of funding a project was very nearly 1 if its ratio exceeded G and very nearly 0 if its ratio did not exceed G. In the continuous-budgeting case this will in fact be true up to the point where the budget is exhausted. It would be desirable, however, to choose G so that it represented the highest ratio likely to permit full utilization of the budget. In the case of batch budgeting, it would similarly be reasonable to choose G so that those projects whose ratios were above it would very nearly match the budget available for investment.

If G were to be thus chosen by headquarters, knowledge of the budget, the divisional search policies, and the divisional opportunity environments would be needed. If G were to be chosen by a division, it would need to know (in addition to its own opportunity environment and its search policy) either:

1. The budget to be made available to it by headquarters

2. The budget available to the firm as well as information about the search policies and opportunity environments of the other divisions

Thus, depending on the actual availability of such information, differing search policies might be chosen by the divisions and by headquarters.

Ranked Projects

A different sort of policy is exemplified by that of evaluating a proposal only if the chances of reversing the prior decision about it exceed some specified value. In this case we assume that a group of projects is on hand and that an initial budget has been made up based on the prior information. To illustrate with a simple case, suppose all projects require roughly the same investment. The prior budget will contain a worst (lowest ranked) project with present worth having a prior mean of P_1. Among those projects not included in the budget will be a best (highest ranked) project with present worth having a prior mean P_2. Now if a project is included in the prior budget, the chances of excluding it (approximately) after evaluation are the chances that the posterior mean of the project will fall below P_2. Actually, of course, if the project is thus excluded, it might later be reincluded on the basis of further evaluation of the other projects. For this reason the above probability is approximate. Similarly, if a project is not included in the budget on the basis of prior information, the probability of reversing this decision is approximately the probability that its posterior mean will fall above P_1. Thus the firm might choose an evaluation policy but apply it only to those projects for which these probabilities of decision reversals exceed some specified value.

This raises the question of the order in which the projects should be evaluated, since the amount of evaluation effort expended may depend on this order. We shall not explore this question but simply suggest that the process might well be begun with those projects whose prior means are nearest P_1 and P_2. These are the projects for which $EVSI$ will tend to be the greatest. For example, the two projects most likely to interchange positions (one included and one excluded from the prior budget) might be considered using the analysis for choosing the best of two projects. This process might be repeated until there are no more pairs of projects for which further investigation can be justified.

Again, a simple example might suggest the obvious point that evaluation policies will generally be different in centralized and decentralized modes of operation. Continuing the assumption that all projects require approximately the same investment, we suppose that two divisions produce exactly m_1 and m_2 proposals respectively. We suppose further that the prior means of the projects being discovered by the firm could be regarded as a uniformly distributed random variable over the range a to b.

Under centralized operation, headquarters has funds to cover B projects that it must choose from the $m = m_1 + m_2$ proposals submitted to it. The expected value of the lowest ranked project in its prior budget will be given by

$$a + (b - a)\frac{m - B + 1}{m + 1}.$$

This is the expected value of P_1, the prior mean of the lowest ranked project in the prior budget. (See Chapter VI.) Under decentralized operation a division has a budget sufficient to fund B_j projects. The expected value of the prior present worth of the lowest ranked project in a division's prior budget will be given by

$$a + (b - a) \frac{m_j - B_j + 1}{m_j + 1}.$$

This will be the average value of P_1 when the division applies the policy. Since the two average values for P_1 will be the same only if

$$\frac{B}{m + 1} = \frac{B_j}{m_j + 1}$$

it will generally be true that headquarters and the divisions will evaluate a given project differently. Note that here again it appears that evaluation policies would be similar if the budget allocation had been approximately in proportion to the number of proposals produced by the search effort.

If headquarters fixes the budget available to a division, the division may be permitted to establish a policy for evaluation that is compatible with this budget, perhaps in the sense outlined above. If, in addition to fixing the divisional budget, headquarters also fixes search policy, we have completely centralized establishment of these policies. On the other hand, if headquarters does not establish in advance the allocation of funds among divisions and permits the divisions to establish their own evaluation (and search) policies, the divisions may be interested in the question of how their choices influence the amount of investment money they receive.

A division that has historically received funding for a large portion of the projects it had proposed will, using the above model, place a greater value on sample information than a division that has obtained funding for a small portion of its projects. The former will thus tend to expend more effort in evaluation than the latter. However, one might expect to observe just the opposite behavior as well. That is, a division that has received funds for only a small portion of its proposals might attempt to improve its record by making a more careful evaluation of those proposals it submits. This might be based on the premise that in ranking proposals, headquarters considers not only the posterior mean of the present worth (M''), but also the posterior variance $[\text{Var}(M'')]$. This is equivalent to saying that headquarters had a utility function that is not linear.[6] The division would thus be attempting to improve its performance by guessing at the headquarters utility function. Of course, headquarters might simply communicate its utility function to the divisions. This would effectively be another means of central determination of evaluation policy.

A still simpler version of a policy that accepts clearly good projects, rejects clearly bad ones, and evaluates only those that are questionable, might be based simply on the mean of the prior probability distribution. That is, one might choose two values of the prior mean of the present worth per dollar of investment. Then projects whose prior mean present worth per dollar of investment fell within this range would be evaluated, whereas others would not. This is a much weaker definition of good and bad projects because it considers only the mean of the prior probability distribution and neglects the variance.

Finally, we consider policies based on the notion that the probability that a project will be funded can be expressed as a function of its expected present worth per dollar of investment. Let $p(M'') =$ the probability of funding a project that has a posterior mean of $\bar{P} = M''$ (this is also a function of the investment in the project). $p(M')$ is similarly defined for the prior mean. If $p(M'')$ were given, the $EVSI$ might be expressed as

$$EVSI = \int_{M''=0}^{\infty} p(M'')M''f(M'')dM'' - p(M')M' .$$

If we take $p(M'') = 0$ for $M'' \leq 0$ and $p(M'') = 1$ for $M'' > 0$, we have the case of ample funds. If we take $p(M'') = 0$ for $M'' \leq Q$ and $p(M'') = 1$ for $M'' > Q$, we have the case discussed above as a possible policy for the ample projects situation. If we take $p(M'')$ to depend on the projects that have previously been discovered and evaluated, then we have a dynamic policy.

Here again, there is little reason to expect that evaluation policies under centralized and decentralized modes of operation will be similar. In the dynamic case, for example, where $p(M'')$ is taken to depend on available funds and on the projects so far discovered and evaluated, a division's policy would correspond to that which might be used by headquarters only if the division was kept continually aware of the projects being proposed by the other divisions and if no final allocation of funds was made until all projects were in.

Evaluation Dynamics

We have previously defined a dynamic evaluation policy as one in which the amount of evaluation effort expended on a proposal depended in part on the characteristics of projects previously discovered and evaluated. We have already encountered one type of dynamic problem. That is, given a batch of projects that are to be evaluated, in what order should they be studied? Various approximate solutions might be proposed, such as allocating evaluation effort sequentially, always seeking to maximize the marginal

ENGSI. Here *ENGSI* might be calculated on the basis of some assumption about the probability of funding a project of the sort we have used above. We may consider two other versions of dynamic evaluation problems.

1. Instead of batch evaluation as suggested above, one may adopt a policy of sequential evaluation of projects as they are discovered. This, for example, would be a necessity in the case of continuous budgeting. If we permit a return to projects previously evaluated for further evaluation in the light of the subsequent emergence, then the problem of developing a good policy may be rather complex.

2. One might modify the policy of sequential evaluation of projects indicated above by not permitting a return to projects previously evaluated. That is, the amount of evaluation effort devoted to a given project may depend on projects previously discovered and evaluated, but not on projects subsequently discovered.

The second problem may be approximated by making the additional assumption that once a project is in the budget, it will not be later displaced. This assumption is made for purposes of computing *EVSI* and is approximate, since in batch budgeting later displacement could occur. We suppose that when a project is discovered, its size is known with certainty. (Size refers to the investment required.) For any given size one could compute the value of the present worth that would have to be exceeded if the project in question is to displace the lowest ranked project or projects in the budget. Then one might assume that if the posterior mean exceeds this value, the project will be funded; otherwise, it will not. This would provide a basis for computing *EVSI* and thus establishing the amount of evaluation effort to be expended.

Search and Evaluation

It will often be useful to consider the processes of search and evaluation as a single process that serves to produce projects for budgeting consideration. In doing this, two general points might be noted. First, prior to the discovery of a project, those attributes that will determine the amount of evaluation effort devoted to it in the case of a static evaluation policy are unknown. These attributes may, however, be viewed as random variables characteristic of the opportunity environment in which search is carried on. This would permit one to consider the average amount of evaluation effort expended on a project from the opportunity environment in question. This average amount of evaluation effort might then be added to the cost of search in the environment to produce a combined average cost for the search-evaluation process. This cost could then be used in planning a combined search-evaluation policy.

Second, in some cases the evaluation process reduces the number of proposals reaching the budgeting stage. For example, in the case of continuous budgeting with ample funds, projects that failed to meet some specified criterion after evaluation might simply be discarded. Thus a portion of the projects discovered would not be funded. This loss would, of course, need to be considered in planning a policy for search and evaluation.

As has been indicated in some of the examples of evaluation policies, search and evaluation may often interact, and thus one might face the task of designing search and evaluation policies compatible with each other as well as with other aspects of the system. Suppose, for example, one uses an evaluation policy that reduces the amount of evaluation effort as the probability of funding a proposal decreases. The larger the number of projects available, the smaller the probability of funding, if this probability is based on the number of proposals competing for a fixed budget. Thus the larger the number of proposals, the smaller the amount of evaluation effort expended per proposal. This tends to reduce the marginal cost of search and evaluation as the number of proposals increases, thus encouraging the production of large numbers of proposals. This may lead to the situation in which a relatively small number of high quality projects are chosen from a large number of proposals without much evaluation effort. We shall subsequently consider more carefully several instances of the problem of matching search and evaluation policies with other aspects of the system. The system design problem is really that of matching policies for (1) search, (2) evaluation, and (3) budgeting, with the allocation of these tasks and budgets throughout the system.

Delegating the Evaluation Function

In some of the systems to be examined, we shall consider the question of where in the organization the evaluation process should be carried on. For example, should the headquarters unit do the evaluation, or should the divisions? Perhaps headquarters should attempt to verify the evaluation performed by the divisions, or perhaps headquarters should do an evaluation independent of that done by a division. At this point we may mention some of the relevant factors that have not been considered in the discussion of the evaluation process up to this point.

Clearly, different organizational units may regard a given proposal as having different prior probability distributions, since available data and experience may well differ. Indeed, one may wish to place the evaluation function at that point in the organization at which the most relevant data, specialized training, and greatest experience is found. This also raises the question of transmitting information generated in one organizational unit to another for evaluation purposes. Expert judgments may be very difficult to express explicitly and thus difficult to transmit. The Bayesian model, however, provides possibly the best available formal structure for making such judgments explicit. Grayson has given an interesting discussion of this point.[7]

One may assume that a division, making evaluations that constitute its justification to headquarters for its request for funds, attempts to be unbiased. Alternatively, one may consider the hypothesis that the division's evaluation is likely to be influenced by its own interests, perhaps as manifested through the rewards system of the organization. This bias may be met by:

1. Subjecting divisional evaluations to various sorts of checks at headquarters

2. Doing post-audits on proposals that are funded, seeking to identify consistent patterns of bias through comparisons of actual project performance with divisional estimates

3. Instituting some system of rewards to division management that make their interest consistent with unbiased evaluations

1. Schlaifer, *op. cit.*

2. This discussion assumes a familiarity with the logic of Bayesian decision theory equivalent to that found in Schlaifer, *op. cit.* Those with more advanced knowledge will find the expository sections unnecessary.

3. The practical justification for the assumption of known variance is given in Schlaifer, *op. cit.*, p. 267. The usefulness of the assumption of normal prior distributions appears on pp. 308–10 of the same work.

4. Schlaifer, *op. cit.*, pp. 10–23, discusses the problem of establishing these prior distributions.

5. To illustrate, consider a sample of size 1. In this case $m = x$. The variance of x is defined as

$$\text{Var}(x) = E(x - m')^2 .$$

This may be operated on as follows:

$$\text{Var}(x) = E(x - m')^2$$
$$= E(x - u + u - m')^2$$
$$= E(x - u)^2 + E(u - m')^2 + 2E(x - u)(u - m')$$
$$= E(x - u)^2 + E(u - m)^2$$
$$= \sigma^2 + \sigma'^2$$

It follows that

$$\text{Var}\,(m) = E(m - m')^2$$
$$= E(m - u)^2 + E(u - m')^2$$
$$= \sigma^2/n + \sigma'^2$$
$$= \sigma^2/n + \sigma^2/n'$$

6. Schlaifer, *op. cit.,* pp. 24–47.

7. C. Jackson Grayson, Jr., *Decisions under Uncertainty: Drilling Decisions by Oil and Gas Operators.* Boston: Division of Research, Graduate School of Business Administration, Harvard University, 1960.

CHAPTER **6**

SOME BASIC MODELS

Introduction

In this chapter the analysis of some very simple capital-budgeting systems is begun. Its aim is to introduce models that express some obvious features of these systems and to suggest some elementary design problems. The analysis is specific and illustrative rather than the source of very general results. Consider a firm that consists of a headquarters group and two "operating" divisions. The history of the firm is divided into time periods usually called budget periods or fiscal years. Within each such period the cycle of activities repeats itself. During a budget period a cash flow will occur. The headquarters group performs the banking and financial management function for the firm. Thus it has full knowledge and control of the funds resulting from the cash flow. The central question in the design of the firm is to what extent it should relinquish control of these funds to the operating divisions.

The objective of the firm is to maximize the (expected) present value of its net worth at the end of the budget period. To do this, it uses the cash flow to carry out the following functions:

1. Searching for investment opportunities
2. Evaluating the opportunities discovered
3. Deciding in which of the opportunities investments will be made

The problem of organizational design is that of determining which of these functions (and to what extent) shall be performed by each of the organizational components. A good design is one that delegates, plans, and controls these activities in accordance with the firm's aim of maximizing the present value of its net worth at the end of the period.

This statement must not be construed narrowly, however, lest it become a foregone conclusion that a completely centralized design is always preferred. The basic measure used to describe the performance of a system during a budget period will certainly be the present value of the increase in net worth achieved during the period. We shall, however, use certain supplementary measures to crudely consider other aspects of various designs. Some systems involve more delay between discovery and investment than others. These delay effects will be noted, and in some cases simple proposals will be made for quantifying their consequences. We shall be interested in the work-load distribution produced by a design in terms of the location in the organization and the time pattern of the evaluation and decision-making tasks. This will permit a very rough first look at the less tangible features of decentralization, such as the incentives for divisional management, suppression of risk, and the allocation of headquarters effort among various tasks (other than capital budgeting). Involved here are the costs and information losses associated with transmitting data on proposed projects, the possible staff duplications, and the differences in the quality of judgments that may appear at different points in the organization. It may be interesting also to use as a crude measure of the degree of decentralization of a given design the proportion of the firm's available capital invested on the basis of decisions made by the divisions. Our general strategy then will be to compare designs using a profile of measures.

We shall suppress for the moment the details of policies for search and evaluation. It will often be assumed that the expected cost of a program of search and evaluation is a linear function of either (1) the number of projects produced by the program, or (2) the level of search and evaluation effort mounted during the budget period. In the latter case the actual number of projects produced will be considered a random function of the level of search and evaluation effort. Designs examined here may be roughly described as: (1) completely centralized, (2) completely decentralized, and (3) decentralized decision-making for clearly desirable opportunities, centralized decision-making for opportunities that are questionable.

Complete Centralization

The basic mode of operation of this system is as follows:

1. The headquarters group is assumed to know the amount of the cash flow F that will become available in the budget period.

Headquarters allocates to each of the operating divisions an amount for search effort.

2. The divisions use their fund allocations to discover investment opportunities. The resulting discoveries are summarized by the divisions in terms of the expected values of their present worths. The expected values of the present worths may be either positive or negative. (The appropriate interest rate has been supplied to the divisions by headquarters). Projects having negative values are discarded, while those with positive values are transmitted to the headquarters group.

3. Opportunities are accumulated at headquarters until the end of the budget period, at which time headquarters invests the remaining available funds in such a way as to maximize the (expected) present value of the firm's net worth.

For the sake of simplicity, we shall assume at first that the initial investment for any opportunity is a known constant; that is, that all opportunities require equal, known, initial investments. Only the initial investment of an opportunity must be funded out of currently available cash. Again for the sake of simplicity, we shall assume that all dollar figures have been divided by this known constant and that the result is an integer whenever fund allocations are being considered.

Let

F = total cash flow available during the budget period (because of the division indicated above, this is also the number of projects that could be funded if all F were to be invested

F_1, F_2 = the amounts allocated for search to Division 1 and Division 2, respectively

m_1, m_2 = the number of opportunities with expected value of present worth greater than zero reported during the budget period by Division 1 and Division 2, respectively

$f_1(m_1), f_2(m_2)$ = probability density functions of m_1 and m_2

The opportunity environment for Division 1 is described by a density function $g_1(r)$, where r is the expected value of the present worth of a project. For this example, we shall assume that $g_1(r) = 1/b_1 - a_1$ for $a_1 \leq r \leq b_1$; and, for Division 2, that $g_2(r) = 1/b_2 - a_2$ for $a_2 \leq r \leq b_2$.

Consider, first, the case in which both divisions search in identical opportunity environments; that is,

$$g_1(r) = g_2(r) = g(r) = \frac{1}{b-a} \qquad \text{for} \qquad a \leq r \leq b.$$

For a particular pair of values m_1 and m_2, let $m = m_1 + m_2$ and let $r(i,m)$ = expected value of the expected present worth of the ith best of m opportunities. Then

$$r(i,m) = a + (b-a)\frac{m-i+1}{m+1}.$$

This follows from the fact that the m values of $r(i,m)$ will divide the area under $g(r)$ into $m+1$ equal parts. Thus the expected value of the present worth of the best of m projects will be

$$a + (b-a)\frac{m}{m+1}.$$

The uniform distribution for $g(r)$ was chosen so as to permit explicit expressions in simple form for these expected values of the present worths of the ranked projects.[1] More generally, however, if $f(r)$ is the distribution that describes the opportunity environment, the expected value of the present worth of the ith ranked of m projects may be found by solving the equation

$$\int_{r=0}^{r(i,m)} f(r)dr = \frac{m-i+1}{m+1}.$$

The problem of allocating search effort in this case may be expressed as the problem of choosing F_1 and F_2 subject to $F_1 + F_2 \leq F$ so as to maximize the expected value of the firm's end-of-period net worth, $\overline{Z}_c$.

The function of $\overline{Z}_c$ may be constructed as follows. If out of the initial funds F, an amount $F_1 + F_2$ is spent for search yielding m opportunities, the headquarters group will rank these opportunities from the largest expected value of present worth on down. It will then invest in the first $F - (F_1 + F_2)$ opportunities, starting at the top of the list. For a particular value of $m \geq F - (F_1 + F_2)$, the expected present worth of the result is

$$Z = \sum_{i=1}^{F-(F_1+F_2)} r(i,m) = \sum_{i=1}^{F-(F_1+F_2)} \left\{ a + (b-a)\frac{m-i+1}{m+1} \right\}.$$

This is the ample projects case in which there are more proposals than can be funded; thus ranking is used to select the best projects for inclusion in the capital budget.

This expression may be simplified in the following way. Letting $B = F - (F_1 + F_2)$, we have

$$Z = \sum_{i=1}^{B} \left\{ a + (b - a) \frac{m - i + 1}{m + 1} \right\} .$$

This may be written

$$Z = Ba + \frac{b - a}{m + 1} (m + m - 1 + m - 2 + \ldots + m - B + 1)$$

which in turn gives

$$Z = B \left\{ a + (b - a) \left(1 - \frac{B + 1}{2(m + 1)} \right) \right\} .$$

For a particular value of $m < F - (F_1 + F_2)$, the expected present worth of the result is

$$\bar{Z} = m \left\{ a + \frac{b - a}{2} \right\} + F - (F_1 + F_2) - m$$

$$= m \left\{ \frac{a + b}{2} - 1 \right\} + F - (F_1 + F_2) .$$

This is the ample funds case in which no ranking takes place. The firm, at the start of the budget period, regards m as a random variable with density function $f(m)$. Thus in planning the allocations for search effort, it will consider

$$\bar{Z}_c = \sum_{m=0}^{F-(F_1+F_2)-1} \left\{ m \left(\frac{a + b}{2} - 1 \right) + F - (F_1 + F_2) \right\} f(m)$$

$$\sum_{m=F-(F_1+F_2)}^{\infty} \left\{ \sum_{i=1}^{F-(F_1+F_2)} r(i, m) \right\} f(m) .$$

This may be written as

$$\bar{Z}_c = \left\{ \frac{a + b}{2} - 1 \right\} \sum_{m=0}^{B-1} mf(m) + B \sum_{m=0}^{B-1} f(m)$$

$$+ \sum_{M=B}^{\infty} \left\{ aB + (b - a) \frac{2Bm - B^2 + B}{2(m + 1)} \right\} f(m)$$

where $B = F - (F_1 + F_2)$.

To restate: The problem of allocating search funds in this case is the problem of maximizing $\overline{Z}_c$ subject to $F_1 + F_2 \leqq F$.

Complete Decentralization

The basic mode of operation for a completely decentralized system is taken to be fully independent search, evaluation, and investment by the divisions. In the most extreme case, cash control and earned surplus are left in the hands of the division. Each division thus neither gives nor receives any capital funds through headquarters and effectively operates as an independent firm. In the less extreme case funds are controlled by headquarters, which allocates them to the divisions. In the context of the previous example this system would begin with the allocation of F_1 to Division 1 and F_2 to Division 2, where $F_1 + F_2 = F$. Each division may then formulate its own search policy and makes its own investment decisions, subject only to the limited funds allocated to it. A lesser degree of decentralization is illustrated by the case in which headquarters, in addition to allocating funds to the divisions, directs the divisions to use a certain portion of their allocations for search.

Consider the case in which headquarters control is limited to the allocation of funds to the divisions. Division 1, receiving an allocation F_1 , must decide on a search policy, say, one of spending an amount S_1 on search effort. The result of this is to produce m_1 proposals among which the division may choose. Search policy involves the problem of choosing S_1 so as to maximize

$$\overline{Z}_1 = \sum_{m_1=0}^{F_1-S_1-1} \left\{ m_1 \left(\frac{a_1 + b_1}{2} - 1 \right) + F_1 - S_1 \right\} f(m_1)$$

$$+ \sum_{m_1=F_1-S_1}^{\infty} \left\{ \sum_{i=1}^{F_1-S_1} r(i, m_1) \right\} f(m_1) .$$

By our previous methods of simplification, this may be written

$$\overline{Z}_1 = \left\{ \frac{a_1 + b_1}{2} - 1 \right\} \sum_{m_1=0}^{B_1-1} m_1 f_1(m_1) + B_1 \sum_{m_1=0}^{B_1-1} f_1(m_1)$$

$$+ \sum_{m_1=B_1}^{\infty} \left\{ a_1 B_1 + (b_1 - a_1) \frac{2B_1 m_1 - B_1^2 + B_1}{2(m_1 + 1)} \right\} f_1(m_1)$$

where $B_1 = F_1 - S_1$.

The result for Division 2 may be similarly expressed. The system result will be

$$\overline{Z}_{DC} = \overline{Z}_1 + \overline{Z}_2 .$$

If we add the assumption of identical opportunity environments, this may be compared with the result achieved by a centralized design, previously expressed as $\overline{Z}_c$.

Some Basic Comparisons

At this point it is possible to demonstrate the basic advantage of centralized capital-budgeting systems so far as investment results are concerned. Suppose the divisions are searching in identical opportunity environments. We consider the case of a centralized design in which search policy has been determined thus yielding a specific value for $B = F - (F_1 + F_2)$. This is to be compared with a decentralized design in which search policy is the same as in the centralized design; that is, the divisions spend the same amount on search in each case. Funds are allocated to the division so that the amount remaining for investment after expenditures for search is B_1 for Division 1 and B_2 for Division 2. The two designs are related in the sense that $B = B_1 + B_2$ and that the probability distributions of the numbers of projects discovered are the same in each case. The result for the centralized design is given by $\overline{Z}_c$ and for the centralized design by

$$\sum_{i=1}^{2} \overline{Z}_i = \overline{Z}_{DC} .$$

Now consider the difference in investment results:

$$D = \overline{Z}_c - \overline{Z}_{DC} .$$

Suppose that $m_1 \leqq B_1$ and $m_2 \leqq B_2$. This will mean ample funds in both designs, and it may be shown that $D = 0$. Thus if funds are ample, no investment advantage exists for either design.

Suppose, as an alternative, that $m_1 + m_2 \leqq B$ and either $m_1 > B_1$ or $m_2 > B_2$. In this case there are ample funds in the centralized design but for only one of the divisions in the decentralized design. Here the centralized design is able to achieve a better matching of funds with opportunities and thus achieve full investment in all of the projects discovered. The decentralized design, however, does not permit investing in some of the opportunities. Thus an advantage accrues to the centralized organization.

Finally, consider the case of ample projects in both designs:

$$m_1 > B_1 \quad \text{and} \quad m_2 > B_2 .$$

The difference in investment results may be written

$$D = \{b - a\} \left\{ \frac{B_1{}^2 + B_1}{2(m_1 + 1)} + \frac{B_2{}^2 + B_2}{2(m_2 + 1)} - \frac{(B_1 + B_2)^2 + B_1 + B_2}{2(m_1 + m_2 + 1)} \right\} .$$

For simplicity we consider the case in which there is an equal distribution of funds $(B_1 = B_2)$, and both divisions discover the same number of opportunities $(m_1 = m_2)$. The difference then becomes

$$D = (b - a) \frac{B_1 m_1 - B_1{}^2}{(m_1 + 1)(2m_1 + .1)} .$$

Expressed in this form, the difference in investment results leads to several hypotheses about the advantages of centralized capital-budgeting systems.

1. The advantage of the centralized design may be "small." For example, if each division has funds sufficient to choose the best 20 of 40 proposed projects, the value of D is roughly 12 per cent of the range of the project present worths. If the present worths vary from $a = 0$ to b, the present worth of the average project is $.5b$; the advantage due to decentralization is roughly 24 per cent of the present worth of an average project.

2. The advantage due to centralization increases as the variability in the project present worths increases. Since we are assuming for the moment that all projects are of size 1, this may be interpreted as the variability in the present worth per dollar of initial investment.

3. If m_1 is fixed and B_1 is allowed to vary subject to the constraint $B_1 < m_1$, the difference D is maximum when $B_1 = .5m$. This may be interpreted by saying that if funds are nearly adequate for the number of proposals, the opportunities for better selection of projects offered by centralization do not have much effect. On the other hand, if there are many projects relative to the funds available, the divisions will have a wide range of choice and be able to select almost as good a set of opportunities as would headquarters in a centralized design.

It may also be noted that for fixed B_1, if m_1 is allowed to vary subject to the constraint $m_1 > B_1$, the value of D first increases and then decreases, as m_1 increases. For fixed B_1, D is maximized for

$$m_1 = B + \sqrt{B^2 + \frac{3B + 1}{8}} .$$

If we fix the ratio of m_1 and B_1, say $B_1 = km_1$, we may consider the effects of expanding both budget and number of projects together. This might be thought of as expanding the scale of operations of the firm. If we use the above ratio to express D as a function of m_1 and take the derivative of the resulting expression, it turns out that the derivative is positive for values of k greater than zero but less than one. Thus we might predict that as the scale of operations of a firm expands, the advantage of the centralization of capital budgeting would tend to increase.

So far it has been assumed that an equal amount would be spent on search by the firm whether operating in the centralized or decentralized mode. This assumption may be examined more closely by considering the behavior of an organizational unit that has a total budget F and sets out to find exactly m opportunities, where the expected cost of such a search program is given by

$$c(m) = \alpha m .$$

Then for $m > F - c(m)$

$$\sum_{i=1}^{F-c(m)} r(i,m) = \left\{ a + (b - a) \frac{2m - F + c(m) + 1}{2(m + 1)} \right\} \{F - c(m)\} .$$

If m is considered for the moment to be a continuous variable, we may set the first derivative of Z equal to zero and solve for the optimal value of m. The result is

$$m = \sqrt{\frac{(b - a)(F + 2)(F + 1)}{3b - a}} - 1$$

for the case $a = 1$.

We may now compare the optimal amount of search for a centralized system with budget F with the optimal amount of search for a two-division decentralized system, where each division has a budget $F_1 = .5F$. Let $m =$ number of projects sought by the centralized firm, and $m_1 =$ number of projects sought by each division of the decentralized firm. From the previous result it follows that

$$\frac{m - 1}{2(m_1 - 1)} = \sqrt{\frac{\dfrac{(b - a)(2F_1 + 2)(2F_1 + 1)}{3b - a}}{\dfrac{4(b - a)(F_1 + 2)(F_1 + 1)}{3b - a}}} .$$

This reduces to

$$\frac{m-1}{2(m_1-1)} = \sqrt{\frac{2F_1+1}{2F_1+4}}.$$

For reasonably large m and m_1 this ratio is approximately the ratio of the number of projects sought by the two designs. The values of the ratio for several values of F_1 are shown below:

F_1	$\dfrac{m-1}{2(m_1-1)}$
5.00	0.89
10.00	.94
20.00	.97
50.00	.99
100.00	.99

Thus one might be justified in the conclusion that major differences in the amount of search will not occur under the assumptions indicated above.

A slightly different and perhaps more conventional way of considering search is to suppose that the investment budget is determined in advance and that search activities are paid for out of other funds and thus do not deplete the investment budget. In this case, the net result for an organizational unit with a budget F that seeks m projects is given by

$$\bar{Z} = F\left\{a + (b-a)\frac{2m-F+1}{2(m+1)}\right\}.$$

Here the optimal values of m satisfies

$$\frac{d\bar{Z}}{dm} = \frac{dc(m)}{dm}$$

and this gives

$$m = \sqrt{(b-a)\frac{F(F+1)}{2}} - 1$$

if $c(m) = m$. Thus under this assumption the organizational unit may carry out different amounts of search than under the previous assumption of a fixed budget for both search and investment.

If, as before, we compare a centralized design with a budget F seeking m

projects with a two-division decentralized design in which each division has a budget $F_1 = .5F$ and seeks m_1 projects, we obtain

$$\frac{m+1}{2(m_1+1)} = \sqrt{\frac{2F_1(2F_1+1)}{4 F_1 (F_1+1)}} = \sqrt{\frac{2F_1+1}{2F_1+2}}$$

which is close to the previous result.

Consider the problem of allocating an investment budget F between two divisions, one of which has discovered m_1 projects and the other of which has discovered m_2 projects. If F_1 and F_2 are the division investment budgets, they would be chosen to satisfy

$$\frac{d\bar{Z}_1}{dF_1} = \frac{d\bar{Z}_2}{dF_2}$$

or

$$b_1 - \frac{(b_1 - a_1)(2F_1+1)}{2(m_1+1)} = b_2 - \frac{(b_2 - a_2)(2F_2+1)}{2(m_2+1)} .$$

If the divisions are searching in identical opportunity environments, this results in the relation

$$\frac{2F_1+1}{2F_2+1} = \frac{m_1+1}{m_2+1} .$$

Thus we could say that in identical opportunity environments the budget allocation should be approximately in proportion to the number of projects that have been or will be discovered by the divisions. Thus our assumption above that the budget allocations would be equal and would be accompanied by equal amounts of search by each division has some basis in reason.

Different Opportunity Environments

We may consider briefly the effects of different opportunity environments for the two divisions. Four problems may be defined here:

1. Suppose the number of projects discovered by each division is fixed, and one wishes to adjust the division budgets in response to this. The desired result may be obtained directly from the relation

$$\frac{d\bar{Z}_1}{dF_1} = \frac{d\bar{Z}_2}{dF_2}$$

given previously.

2. Suppose the divisional budgets are fixed, and one wishes to establish a search policy (m_1, m_2) that will be optimal for these budgets. This can be obtained from the expression for the optimal value of m already derived.

3. Next, suppose we are free to choose F_1, F_2, m_1, and m_2 for two divisions searching in different opportunity environments, subject to the constraint $F_1 + F_2 = F$. The values of the m_i $(i + 1, 2)$ must satisfy

$$m_i = \sqrt{(b_i - a_i)\frac{F_i(F_i + 1)}{2}} - 1 \cong F_i \sqrt{\frac{b_i - a_i}{2}} - 1 .$$

Substituting the approximation into the expression for Z_i and simplifying yields

$$Z_i = F_i\left\{b_i - \sqrt{\frac{b_i - a_i}{2}}\right\} - \sqrt{\frac{b_i - a_i}{2}} .$$

If we take the derivatives,

$$\frac{dZ_i}{dF_i} = b_i - \sqrt{\frac{b_i - a_i}{2}} .$$

Thus the derivatives are constant, and an optimal allocation of search effort and investment funds will always involve searching and investing in only one environment. Under these assumptions centralization would lead effectively to one division remaining static so far as investment in a given budget period is concerned. In subsequent budget periods, of course, the opportunity environments might change.

4. Suppose now a centralized scheme in which the firm arranges search effort so that Division 1 produces m_1 proposals and Division 2 produces m_2 proposals. The headquarters group then ranks the $m = m_1 + m_2$ proposals and chooses the best F of them.

Let $p = m_1/m$ and $r(i,m)$ = the expected value of the present worth for the ith ranked of m projects. These satisfy the relation

$$p = \int_{r=r(i,m)}^{\infty} g_1(r)dr + (1 - p) \int_{r=r(i,m)}^{\infty} g_2(r)dr = \frac{i}{m + 1} .$$

If

$$g_1(r) = \frac{1}{b_1 - a_1} \quad \text{and} \quad g_2(r) = \frac{1}{b_2 - a_2} ,$$

then solving the above relation for $r(i,m)$ yields

$$r(i,m) = \frac{(b_1 - a_1)(1 - p)b_2 + (b_2 - a_2)pb_1 - \dfrac{i}{m+1}(b_2 - a_2)(b_1 - a_1)}{(b_1 - a_1)(1 - p) + (b_2 - a_2)p}.$$

Now, if F projects are to be funded, the expected investment result is given by

$$\sum_{i=1}^{F} r(i,m) = \frac{F\left\{(b_1 - a_1)(1 - p)b_2 + (b_2 - a_2)pb_1 - \dfrac{F(F+1)}{2(m+1)}(b_2 - a_2)(b_1 - a_1)\right\}}{(b_1 - a_1)(1 - p) + (b_2 - a_2)p}.$$

This will be maximized by choosing either $p = 0$ or $p = 1$. Thus again, search and investment will be exclusively in one division rather than allocated between the two divisions.

A proof that this result holds, or does not hold generally, has not been obtained. However, for many examples it does appear that search and investment would be limited to one division and one opportunity environment. It is important to note here that there are of course other reasons for allocating search and investment among different opportunity environments.

1. This may be done as a part of a program of diversification aimed at trading some expected gain for a reduction in risk.

2. Other budgeting procedures and other rules for selection of investments to be funded may be used that do lead to some allocation of funds among environments. Several of these will be examined in later sections.

3. As has been pointed out, in some firms the generation of investment proposals is a process implicit in the conduct of the firm's business. Thus without deliberate control by management, proposals flow in from various opportunity environments. There would be an occasional good proposal from an environment that, on the average, was rather poor.

4. An investment in a division may represent

   a) An effort to maintain the status of the division as a possible generator of good proposals in the future

   b) An attempt to preserve the morale or increase the incentives for a division

   c) The fulfilment of a tacit past commitment to give the division its share

5. If search is within control of the divisions and funding decisions are made at headquarters, one would expect that a division whose opportunity environment was relatively poor might generate a large number of proposals so as to get its "share" of the available capital budget.

In many of the models that follow we have assumed that the divisions are operating in identical opportunity environments. This not only makes for mathematical simplicity but suppresses the effects of the environments in favor of other effects we wish to study, and creates situations in which there is, as in reality, some motivation to allocate funds among environments.

Continuous Budgeting

Holding proposals until the end of a budget period implies that the resulting delay in implementation is less costly than the lack of selectivity in a continuous-budgeting policy. Continuous budgeting may be of interest where delays are important and may be implemented with a policy such as, "All proposals having a present worth per dollar invested greater than some specified amount will be funded immediately." If such a policy were to be used in a centralized system where proposals were ample relative to investment funds available, the advantages of centralization due to greater selectivity disappear. Indeed, investment results would be no different on the average from those obtained by a decentralized system in which each division used the same policy and had ample proposals for its funds.

If there is the possibility that a decentralized division may not obtain sufficient proposals of the specified quality, some of the firm's funds may not be invested. Under such conditions a centralized design would offer greater possibilities for avoiding imbalances between funds and proposals. If the number of proposals resulting from a given level of search effort is a random variable, one might wish to choose this level so that the probability of proposals being adequate is fixed at some level. Under such a policy a centralized design would require less search effort than a decentralized one. Clearly, the flow of proposals can be regulated not only by choosing levels of search effort but by varying the present worth per dollar cutoff value for funding under continuous budgeting. If search effort is fixed, it would be desirable to raise this cutoff value as high as possible while preserving some specified level of risk that proposals will not be adequate.

A continuous-budgeting system in a decentralized firm would in actuality include some obvious additional complications. If a division had excess funds at the end of a budget period, these might be recovered by headquarters. If, in turn, a division had proposals available at the end of a period, these might also be sent along to headquarters. In this way some of the obvious imbalances would be corrected. These complications lead directly to the notion of partial decentralization based on project quality or present worth per dollar of investment.[2]

Partial Decentralization

One form of partial decentralization is based on the principle that the divisions may invest in clearly desirable proposals, whereas those that are questionable must be sent to headquarters for a final decision. Such a design may stem from the belief that

1. A "clearly desirable" project is one that appears to have a relatively high present worth per dollar of investment and thus is likely to be included in any capital budget, whether or not the decision is delegated. There is little point in submitting such projects to headquarters for a "rubber stamp."

2. A clearly desirable project is one that looks very good both in the judgment of the division and in the judgment of the headquarters group. It may be further characterized by agreement as to the (relatively modest) amount of evaluation effort appropriate. This is perhaps what is meant by the remark that headquarters can "trust" the divisions to make the decision on such projects.

The major design variable in such a scheme is the choice of a value of present worth per dollar of investment that defines clearly desirable proposals. Obviously, the higher this value, the greater the degree of centralization. One would generally expect that the investment results from partial decentralization would, if budgets and search levels are fixed, be intermediate between those of full centralization and full decentralization described previously. The analysis may be directly modified to show this.

Partial decentralization raises certain other design questions that will be examined in subsequent sections. For example:

1. Should there be a limit on the total investment by a division in a given budget period, or should the division be permitted to fund all of the good proposals that come to its attention?

2. Should search policy be dictated by headquarters or delegated to the divisions?

3. What will be the effects on the distribution of decision-making work loads and the delays in implementation of a policy of partial decentralization?

Before considering these questions, we shall reconsider the assumption that all proposals have identical initial investment.

Projects with Varying Size

Consider the initial investment in a project (its size) to be a random variable x, with probability distribution $f(x)$. Assume that projects are ranked according to present worth per dollar of initial investment. Let $r(i,m)$ = the present worth per dollar invested for the ith ranked of m projects (on the average). As before, we shall assume that the present worth multiplier is a uniformly distributed random variable over the range from a to b. We also assume it to be independent of the size of the project. The expected value of the present worth of the ith ranked of m projects is then

$$r(i,m) \int_{z} xf(x)dx = \bar{x}r(i,m).$$

If n projects are funded, the total initial investment will be

$$X_n = x_1 + x_2 + \ldots + x_n$$

where x_1 is the size of the first project funded, and so on.

Consider the situation in which a fixed budget amount B is available. Two cases may be usefully distinguished. In the first case, minor adjustments of the size of projects may be made permitting the projects funded to consume exactly the budget amount B. In the second case, no such adjustments in project size are permitted; thus, generally, the projects chosen will not use exactly B dollars in initial investment.

Case I

As many projects as will consume the budget B are selected, beginning with the top-ranked project and proceeding down the list. Minor adjustments are made so that exactly B dollars are invested. Let $p(n,B)$ = the probability that this process will result in exactly n projects' being funded using a budget of B (assuming ample projects). The average project size is then assumed to be B/n. If the number of projects that are available, m, is always greater than n, it follows that for fixed m and for n less than m

$$\bar{Z} = \sum_{n=1}^{m} \frac{Bn}{n} \left\{ a + (b-a)\frac{2m-n+1}{2(m+1)} \right\} p(n,B)$$

$$= Ba + B(b-a)\left\{ \frac{2m+1}{2(m+1)}(1-p(0,B)) - \frac{\bar{n}_B}{2(m+1)} \right\}$$

where $\bar{n}_B$ = the expected number of projects funded with a budget of B. Now assume that $p(0,B) = 0$. Then

$$\bar{Z} = Ba + B(b - a)\left\{1 - \frac{\bar{n}_B + 1}{2(m + 1)}\right\}$$

$$= Bb + B(b - a)\frac{\bar{n}_B + 1}{2(m + 1)}.$$

This result reduces to that under the previous assumption of fixed project size equal to 1 if we let $\bar{n}_B = B$.

Assume that the number of projects available m is a random variable with distribution $f(m)$, and that m is unlikely to be less than n. Taking the expectation with respect to m, we have

$$\bar{Z} = Bb - \frac{B(b - a)(\bar{n}_B + 1)}{2}\sum_{m=0}^{\infty}\frac{1}{m + 1}f(m).$$

In the special case in which m is Poisson,

$$f(m) = \frac{e^{-2}}{m}\lambda m$$

$$\sum_{m=0}^{\infty}\frac{1}{m + 1}f(m) = \sum_{m=0}^{\infty}\frac{1}{\lambda}f(m + 1) = \frac{1}{\lambda}.$$

This reduces to

$$\bar{Z} = Bb - \frac{B(b - a)(\bar{n}_B + 1)}{2}.$$

Here again, if we let $\bar{n}_B = B$, this reduces to the result obtained previously under the assumption that all projects were of fixed size equal to 1.

Dropping the assumption that m is unlikely to be less than n, we have for a given m

$$\bar{Z} = \sum_{n=1}^{m}B\left\{a + (b - a)\frac{2m - n + 1}{2(m + 1)}\right\}p(n,B)$$

$$+ \sum_{n=m+1}^{\infty}\left\{m\bar{x}\frac{a + b}{2} + B - m\bar{x}\right\}p(n,B).$$

We may then take the expected value of this quantity with respect to m.

Here we encounter the difficulty of the mixed case; that is, if funds are ample or if projects are ample, the analysis may be carried on with reasonable facility. If, however, funds are sometimes ample and at other times projects are ample, the analysis is difficult.

Case II

Assume no adjustments are permitted and let $f_n(X_n) =$ the probability distribution of the total investment in n projects, and $P(n,B) =$ the probability that the number of projects funded in a budget B is less than or equal to n. Then

$$P(n,B) = \int_{X_{n+1}=B}^{\infty} f_{n+1}(X_{n+1})dX_{n+1}$$

and

$$p(n,B) = P(n,B) - P(n-1,B).$$

For example, if project size is a normally distributed random variable, the X_n will also be normal, and $p(n,B)$ might be computed from the table of the cumulative normal distribution using the above expression.

With the probability distribution of n established on the assumption that no adjustments in project size are to be made, we may assume further that adjustments can be made in order to simplify consideration of the fact that n projects require exactly B dollars in initial investment. We assume, in particular, that although $p(n,B)$ is determined in the above manner, adjustments in project size are subsequently made that do not alter n but that exhaust the available budget B.

Example

Let us suppose that project size is a random variable with a negative exponential probability distribution. Then $p(n,B)$ is Poisson. If no adjustments in project size are permitted, the n projects $(n \geq 1)$ will on the average require an initial investment equal to

$$\frac{n}{n+1}B.$$

That is to say, given that n projects are funded using a budget of B dollars, the average amount of money left over (uninvested) is

$$\frac{B}{n+1}.$$

For large n, the assumption of adjustments in size is not important because the amount left over becomes small. Note also that without adjustments, the average project size, given that n projects are funded with a budget of B, is

$$\frac{B}{n+1} \qquad (n \geq 1).$$

If adjustments are assumed, the average project size is simply B/n. For large n these two quantities differ only slightly. These results are shown as follows:

$$f(x) = \alpha e^{-\alpha x}$$

$$p(n,B) = e^{-\alpha B} \frac{(\alpha B)^n}{n!}$$

$$p(0,B) = e^{-\alpha B}$$

$$\int_{x=B}^{\infty} \alpha e^{-\alpha x} dx = e^{-\alpha B}$$

$$E(x) = \int_{x=0}^{\infty} x f(x) dx = \frac{1}{\alpha}$$

Let $E(x|n)$ = expected project size given that n projects are funded with a budget B. It must be that

$$E(x) = \sum_{n=0}^{\infty} E(x|n) p(n,B) = \frac{1}{\alpha} \cdot$$

Suppose we assume that

$$E(x|n) = \frac{B}{n+1} \qquad \text{for} \qquad n \geq 1.$$

Then it must follow that

$$E(x) = \sum_{n=1}^{\infty} \frac{B}{n+1} e^{-\alpha B} \frac{(\alpha B)^n}{n!} + E(x|n=0)e^{-\alpha} = \frac{1}{\alpha} \cdot$$

Noting that

$$E(x|n=0) = \int_{x=B}^{\infty} x \alpha e^{-\alpha x} dx \left\{ \frac{1}{e^{-\alpha B}} \right\} = B + \frac{1}{\alpha},$$

we have

$$E(x) = \frac{1}{\alpha}(1 - \alpha B e^{-\alpha B} - e^{-\alpha B}) + \left(B + \frac{1}{\alpha}\right) e^{-\alpha B} = \frac{1}{\alpha} \cdot$$

Thus the assumption is proved.

Next we require an expression for $\bar{n}_B$ = the expected number of projects funded in a budget of size B.

$$\bar{n}_B = \sum_{n} n p(n,B)$$

In particular, we require $\bar{n}_B$ in terms of B and $E(x)$. Let $E(x|n,B)$ = the expected project size given that n projects are funded in a budget B. If we use the adjustment assumption,

$$E(x|n,B) = \frac{B}{n} \cdot$$

This is also approximately true for large n, even if adjustments are not made. Then

$$E(x) = \sum_{n} E(x|n,B) p(n,B)$$

$$= \sum_{n} \frac{B}{n} p(n,B)$$

where we assume $p(0,B) = 0$.

This leads to the expression

$$\frac{1}{\displaystyle\sum_{n} \frac{1}{n} p(n,B)} = \frac{B}{E(x)} \cdot$$

At this point considerable simplicity may be achieved if one assumes

$$\bar{n}_B \cong \frac{1}{\displaystyle\sum_{n} \frac{1}{n} p(n,B)}$$

for

$$(n \geq 1)$$

and thus

$$\bar{n}_B \cong \frac{B}{E(x)} \, .$$

This approximation appears to be good if n is restricted to large values and improves as the variance of n decreases. It may be noted in the cases where $p(n,B)$ is binomial or Poisson and no adjustments are made, the expression

$$\bar{n}_B = \frac{B}{E(x)}$$

is exact.

In what follows it will be generally assumed that

$$\bar{n}_B = \frac{B}{E(x)} \, .$$

Suppose, for example, $p(n,B)$ is of the form

$$\frac{B!}{n!(B-n)!} \, q^n(1-q)^{B-n} \, .$$

Then

$$\bar{n}_B = \sum_n np(n,B) = Bq \, .$$

The size of a project, x, has distribution

$$f(x) = (1-q)^{x-1}q$$

with mean

$$\bar{x} = \frac{1}{q} \, .$$

A Second Model

At this point some of the assumptions made originally may be slightly relaxed without losing the tractability of the model. Suppose, for example, that the process of discovering opportunities is a Poisson process with parameter λ. The cost of a level of search effort that will yield opportunities at mean rate is

$$C_1(\lambda_1) = \alpha_1\lambda_1$$

for Division 1, and

$$C_2(\lambda_2) = \beta_1\lambda_2$$

for Division 2.

Thus for an allocation of funds to Division 1 of F_1 a level of search effort may be mounted such that

$$C_1(\lambda_1) = F_1 .$$

As a result, m_1 opportunities will be discovered, with

$$f_1(m_1) = \frac{e^{-\lambda_1 T}(\lambda_1 T)^{m_1}}{m_1!} .$$

The situation is similar for Division 2. Here T is the length of the budget period, which may be taken equal to 1. The total number of proposals $m = m_1 + m_2$ will be a random variable having a Poisson density function with mean $\lambda_1 + \lambda_2$.

We shall continue the assumption that the divisions are searching in identical opportunity environments but drop the assumption that all projects are of fixed size with respect to initial investment. We consider the case of ample projects, since it is here that the effects of decentralization on investment results appear. The ample-projects assumption here takes the form of assuming that the number of projects that may be funded with a budget B—say, n—is unlikely to be more than the number of proposals available. We consider only search policies for which this assumption reasonably holds. It has been shown that under these conditions for a fixed number of proposals (n)

$$\bar{Z} = Bb - B(b - a)\frac{\bar{n}_B + 1}{2(m + 1)}$$

where $\bar{n}_B = $ the expected number of projects funded with a budget of B .

We further assume that

$$\bar{n}_B = \frac{B}{E(x)}$$

where $E(x) = $ the average size of a project with respect to initial investment. Then

$$\bar{Z} = Bb - \frac{(b - a)B(B + E(x))}{2E(x)(m + 1)} .$$

Next, we take the expected value of $\bar{Z}$ with respect to m under the Poisson assumption given above. The lower limit on m must be n (which is itself a random variable); but we are assuming that the probability of m's being less than n is small, and thus taking the lower limit of m to be zero yields a suitable approximation.

$$\bar{Z}_c = \sum_{m=0}^{\infty} \left\{ Bb - \frac{(b-a)B(B+E(x))}{2E(x)(m+1)} \right\} f(m)$$

$$= Bb - \frac{(b-a)B(B+E(x))}{2E(x)(\lambda_1 + \lambda_2)} \ .$$

Now if the unit search costs are equal $a_1 = \beta_1$ and $B = F - F_1 - F_2 = F - S$, then $\lambda_1 + \lambda_2 = S/a_1 = KS$. The optimal search budget for a centralized organization is obtained by solving

$$\frac{d\bar{Z}c}{dS} = 0 \ .$$

This yields

$$S = \sqrt{\frac{F^2 + FE(x)}{2bKE(x)} + 1} \ .$$

In similar fashion the optimal search budget for, say, Division 1 will be

$$S_1 = \sqrt{\frac{F_1^2 + F_1E(x)}{2bKE(x)} + 1}$$

where F_1 = total funds allocated to Division 1.

Under these assumptions slightly less will be spent on search in the centralized design. However, it is convenient to consider that the optimal amount of search expenditure is approximately proportional to the available funds; that is,

$$S = \sqrt{\frac{F^2 + FE(x)}{2bKE(x)} + 1} \cong F\sqrt{\frac{b-a}{2bKE(x) + b - a}} = \alpha F \ .$$

With this approximation equal amounts will be spent for search by the centralized and the decentralized systems.[3] The advantage of centralization is, then, in better investment results. This may be estimated by noting that the difference in investment results may be reduced to an expression of the form

$$\bar{Z}_C - \bar{Z}_{DC} = \frac{b - a}{2KE(x)} \left\{ \frac{1}{\alpha} - 1 \right\}.$$

Since α must always be less than 1, there will always be an advantage for centralization in terms of investment results.

Under these assumptions the advantage resulting from centralization does not depend on the scale of operations of the firm nor on the allocation of funds between the two divisions. As we saw in the previous model, the advantage tends to increase as the variability in the present worth per investment dollar increases. Here it appears that the advantage decreases as the average project size increases and as the cost of search $(1/K)$ decreases.

We can obtain similar results in somewhat simpler fashion if we assume that the investment budget is fixed in advance and that search expenditures are met out of other funds. In this case, we may consider an organization unit with investment budget B and search costs given by

$$C(\lambda) = \alpha_0 + \alpha_1\lambda.$$

Investment results will be

$$\bar{Z} = Bb - (b - a) \frac{B^2 + BE(x)}{2 E(x)}$$

then

$$\frac{d\bar{Z}}{d\lambda} = (b - a) \frac{B^2 + BE(X)}{2\lambda^2 E(x)} \quad \text{and} \quad \frac{dC(\lambda)}{d\lambda} = \alpha_1.$$

Setting

$$\frac{d\bar{Z}}{d\lambda} = \frac{dC(\lambda)}{d\lambda}$$

yields

$$\frac{b - a}{2E(x)} (B^2 + BE(x)) = \lambda^2 \alpha_1$$

$$\lambda = \sqrt{\frac{(b - a)(B^2 + BE(x))}{2\alpha_1 E(x)}}.$$

If we once again make the convenient approximation that

$$\lambda = B\sqrt{\frac{b - a}{2\alpha_1 E(x)}}$$

then the same amount of search effort will be used by centralized and decentralized systems, assuming search costs are equal for the divisions.

Suppose we consider a firm consisting of d divisions, each searching in identical environments with identical search-cost functions. Suppose further that each division generates proposals at mean rate λ. A centralized design would yield

$$\bar{Z}_c = Bb - \frac{(b-a)B(B+E(x))}{2d\lambda E(x)}.$$

This might be compared with a decentralized design in which each division received an allocation of funds equal to B/d.

$$\bar{Z}_{DC} = d\left\{\frac{B}{d}b - \frac{(b-a)\left(\frac{B}{d}\right)\left(\frac{B}{d}+E(x)\right)}{2\lambda E(x)}\right\}$$

$$D = \bar{Z}_c - \bar{Z}_{DC} = \frac{(b-a)B}{2\lambda E(x)}\left\{\frac{B}{d}+E(x)-\frac{B+1}{d}\right\}$$

$$= \frac{(b-a)B}{2\lambda E(x)}\left\{\frac{dE(x)-1}{d}\right\}$$

Using the approximation for λ gives

$$D = \sqrt{\frac{(b-a)\alpha_1}{2E(x)}}\left\{\frac{dE(x)-1}{d}\right\}.$$

This relation suggests the same hypotheses as the previous one, in addition to the idea that the advantage of centralization increases as the number of divisions increases under the assumptions made here.

Partial Decentralization with Ample Projects

We turn to the system of partial decentralization based on the principle that divisions are authorized to undertake clearly good projects, but questionable ones must be sent up to headquarters for study. Here, clearly, good projects are defined as those with present worth per dollar of investment above some cutoff value c. It is assumed that the divisions search in identical opportunity environments and operate with equal cutoff values. To these assumptions we add the following:

1. Varying project sizes.

2. Search produces a Poisson stream of projects.

3. Headquarters imposes upon each division a budget limit on the total investment in clearly good projects that may be undertaken. This is assumed to result in batch budgeting throughout.

4. Levels of search effort are such that the ample projects assumption holds at each division.

Investment results for division i, operating with budget restriction B_i, may be expressed as

$$\bar{Z}_i = B_i b - (b - c) \frac{B_i(B_i + E(x))}{2 \dfrac{b - c}{b - a} \lambda_i E(x)}$$

$$= B_i b - (b - a) \frac{B_i(B_i + E(x))}{2\lambda_i E(x)}.$$

It is interesting to note that with these particular assumptions if the distribution of the opportunity environment is uniform, the cutoff level c plays no role in the investment results achieved by the divisions. As the cutoff level is increased, the divisions have fewer projects among which to choose, but the projects available have higher present worths per dollar. These two effects are exactly compensatory, permitting the investment results to be independent of the cutoff value.

If each division is free to choose its own level of search effort and does so considering only its budget B_i and the cost of search, the amount of search will generally be different than in a completely centralized or decentralized design. If the marginal cost of search is a, and is the same for each division, the level of search effort chosen will be

$$\lambda_i = \sqrt{\frac{(b - a)(B_i^2 + B_i E(x))}{2\alpha E(x)}}$$

as has been shown previously. If we make the approximation that

$$\lambda_i = B_i \sqrt{\frac{b - a}{2\alpha E(x)}} = KB_i$$

then for partial decentralization

$$\sum_i \lambda_i = K \sum_i B_i$$

and for either fully centralized or fully decentralized plans

$$\sum_i \lambda_i = KB.$$

Since, under a partially decentralized scheme, headquarters retains some of the firm's funds,

$$\sum_i B_i < B,$$

and thus the partial decentralization policy results in less search if the divisions take this limited viewpoint.

As alternatives to this decentralization of the search-policy decision, one might consider:

1. Headquarters dictates search policy to the divisions.

2. The divisions take the view that what we are calling the investment results achieved by headquarters are really investments in divisional activity. Each division then tries to regulate its search effort in terms of its own investment results and those it expects headquarters to achieve on its behalf.

Each of these alternatives will be considered briefly.

Headquarters Dictation of Search Policy

Suppose we make the simple but not particularly realistic supposition that at the end of a budget period any projects that are clearly good but not funded by the divisions are discarded. This will mean that headquarters will choose among the questionable projects submitted by the divisions. If the funds retained by headquarters are in amount B_h, its investment results will be

$$\bar{Z}_h = B_h c - (c - a) \frac{B_h(B_h + E(x))}{2 \frac{c - a}{b - a} \sum_i \lambda_i E(x)}$$

$$= B_h c - (b - a) \frac{B_h(B_h + E(x))}{2 \sum_i \lambda_i E(x)}.$$

On the assumption that the supply of questionable projects is ample at headquarters and the divisions, the system results may be written

$$\bar{Z} = \bar{Z}_h + \sum_i \bar{Z}_i.$$

In this system investment results may be improved by increasing the cutoff value c or by reducing the headquarters budget and thus increasing the division budgets. In considering these effects, one must be careful to preserve the ample-projects assumption throughout the system.

If one compares this system with a fully decentralized system with the divisions doing equal amounts of search in either case, the partially decentralized system does not achieve as large investment results. This is because funds invested by headquarters yield a lower present worth per dollar than those invested by the divisions. Thus it follows that for equal amounts of search, partial decentralization is less successful than complete centralization or complete decentralization, in terms of investment results.

It also appears that a partially decentralized system will, even if search policy is chosen optimally by headquarters and dictated to the divisions, result in less search effort.

Suppose, for purposes of illustration, that there are two divisions. Let

$$\lambda_1^* + \lambda_2 = \lambda$$

$$\lambda_1 = K\lambda$$

for

$$0 < K < 1.$$

Headquarters then chooses to satisfy

$$\frac{d\bar{Z}}{d\lambda} = \alpha$$

$$\frac{d\bar{Z}}{d\lambda} = \frac{b - a}{2E(x)} \left\{ \frac{B_h(B_h + E(x))}{\lambda^2} + \frac{B_1(B_1 + E(x))}{K\lambda^2} + \frac{B_2(B_2 + E(x))}{(1 - K)\lambda^2} \right\} = \alpha.$$

Thus

$$\lambda = \sqrt{\frac{b - a}{2\alpha E(x)} \left\{ B_h(B_h + E(x)) + \frac{B_1(B_1 + E(x))}{K} + \frac{B_2(B_2 + E(x))}{1 - K} \right\}}.$$

Now, since the two divisions are searching in identical opportunity environments, we shall suppose that headquarters finds it reasonable to give them equal budgets. Having done this, headquarters wishes to make the marginal payoff for search $d\bar{Z}/d\lambda_i$ equal at the two divisions. This will result in setting $K = 1 - K = .5$. The above expression may then be written

$$\lambda = \sqrt{\frac{b - a}{2\alpha E(x)} \left\{ B_h(B_h + E(x)) + 4B_1(B_1 + E(x)) \right\}}.$$

It may be shown that this is less than that for a centralized system:

$$\lambda = \sqrt{\frac{b - a}{2\alpha E(x)} B(B + E(x))}$$

where $B = B_h + 2B_1$. Since a fully decentralized system will require slightly more, or an equal amount of, search than a centralized system, the result is established.

Division Consideration of Headquarters Results

As a second alternative to the establishment of search policy by the divisions on the basis of their own budgets, suppose a division wishes to base its search policy on its own results plus its share of those achieved by headquarters. For example, suppose a division reasons that it will share in headquarters results in proportion to the relative number of projects it submits to headquarters. Thus a division views its payoff as

$$\bar{Z}_i = B_i b - (b - a) \frac{B_i(B_i + E(x))}{2\lambda_i E(x)} + \frac{\lambda_i}{\sum_j \lambda_j} \bar{Z}_h \, .$$

The important point is that a single division cannot appropriately choose such a search policy without knowing the level of search effort chosen by every other division as well as the budget available at headquarters. Thus a high degree of co-ordination would be required among the divisions, which could probably be effectively achieved only through considerable centralization.

Forwarding Excess Projects

Instead of the previous assumption that projects not funded by the divisions are discarded, one might better assume that these projects are forwarded to headquarters. Headquarters, in turn, considers them in budgeting the funds it has retained. Although it is difficult to represent such systems mathematically, one would expect that when excess projects are not discarded by the division, partially decentralized systems will produce better investment results than fully decentralized systems but not yield such good results as fully centralized systems.

Partial decentralization based on the size of initial investment is both easier to analyze and more commonly practiced. These sorts of systems will be examined in subsequent chapters.

Evaluation under Partial Decentralization

Suppose we assume that one reason why headquarters elects a policy of permitting the divisions to fund a limited budget of clearly good projects is that there is some measure of common agreement throughout the firm as to which projects are "clearly good." The implication is that what is regarded by the divisions (after discovery but prior to further evaluation) as a good project will also be regarded by the headquarters group as a good project. If it were otherwise, headquarters might be reluctant to delegate to any degree. There remains the question of whether or not the determination of policies for evaluation should be delegated. Since it will often be the case that some particular organizational unit is clearly in the best position to obtain certain information, we are concerned not with who gets the data but rather with who decides what information is to be obtained.

Consider the "clearly good" projects, and suppose that any such projects not funded by the divisions are submitted to headquarters for funding at the end of the budget period. Under these conditions both headquarters and the divisions would share in the belief that a clearly good project is certain to be funded and thus come to a common conclusion on how much evaluation effort should be devoted to such a project. Thus so far as these good projects are concerned, there would be little difference in the amount of search effort expended by the firm regardless of whether or not the decision is delegated.

If good projects not funded by the divisions are discarded rather than being sent to headquarters, the evaluation effort devoted to a project will depend perhaps on the probability of the project's being funded. Now if the level of search effort and the division budgets are taken as given, presumably headquarters and the divisions will come to similar conclusions on this probability and thus on evaluation policy.

If the divisions are free to choose a level of search effort and a policy for evaluation of good projects, to the extent that headquarters will differ in its choice of search efforts, so it will also differ in its choice of evaluation policy. Since, generally speaking, a good project is one that justifies relatively little further evaluation effort, the differences may not be of great importance. Thus there may be justification for delegating evaluation decisions on clearly good projects to the divisions themselves.

Evaluation policy for those projects not in the class of clearly good ones is less likely to be left to the discretion of the divisions. Unless each division knows the amount of money available at headquarters and the levels of search effort (as well as the opportunity environments) of the other divisions, it has slim grounds for estimating the chances that a project will be funded and thus little basis for establishing an evaluation policy. The remarks made in connection with search policy apply here as well.

If one wishes to consider problems involving restrictions on the total amount of evaluation effort expended by the firm, or dynamic evaluation policies, a greater degree of interdependence will exist among the activities of the organizational units. Thus the advantages of centralization tend to be increased.

Work Load and Delay Effects

So far as investment results are concerned, the advantage appears to be on the side of the centralized designs examined. Advantages on the side of decentralized designs may appear in forms such as incentives for management; reductions in the delay associated with implementing a proposal; better judgments on the part of decision-makers due to better information; avoidance of the costs, delays, and information loss involved in transmitting proposals to headquarters; and more appropriate distribution of executive work loads. Most of these effects would appear difficult to evaluate in operational terms. They tend to be in the realm of "intangibles." It may be of some interest, however, to examine briefly the problems of work-load distribution and delay to give some idea of the dimensions of their consequences, if not the costs involved.

For simplicity, it might be supposed that the process that follows the emergence of a proposal consists of:

1. *Transmission.*—This includes preparing the proposal in suitable form, sending it, and, possibly, presenting it to the appropriate agency.

2. *Evaluation.*—This may be done before or after transmission depending on which organizational unit is assigned this task.

3. *Delay prior to decision.*—If batch budgeting is being used, then decision is delayed until the batch has been considered. Under continuous budgeting congestion may occur, and a proposal may have to wait until those ahead of it have been disposed of.

4. *Decision.*—In the case of batch budgeting the time required may depend on the number of projects in the batch.

The costs of having a proposal delayed for various lengths of time by this process will generally be difficult to state. Some projects may be handled well in advance of the time at which they can be implemented; thus delays are of no particular significance. Other projects may permit compensation for delays through acceleration of some phases of implementation, an action usually difficult to evaluate. It is often the case that delays have consequences for customer satisfaction or market timing that are also difficult to express in operational terms. Thus the notion of the cost of a delay in implementing a project must not be taken too seriously. We shall be content to make some rough statements about the order of magnitude of some types of delay.

The decision-making work load is likewise most difficult to evaluate in monetary terms. The work load may be expressed both in terms of the total number of projects considered in a budget period and in terms of the distribution of this effort over the period. Both of these things influence the amount and pattern of time available for other activities. The value of this time pattern is difficult to express generally. The work load is also a function of the effort expended by others in the organization on evaluating and communicating the proposals. All of this is further compounded by the differing qualities of judgments made by various decision-makers in the firm and the possible alternative uses for their time.

To illustrate some of the immediate observations that might be made about work-load distributions and delay, we consider comparisons between fully centralized and fully decentralized systems. In either sort of system the decision-making unit may elect continuous budgeting, budgeting at fixed time intervals, budgeting when a fixed number of projects are available for consideration, or some other more complex policy.[4] Thus one might be interested in comparing a centralized design using continuous budgeting with a decentralized design using batch budgeting. Though not all possible pairs of systems are interesting, a few may be usefully examined.

Batch Budgeting

A fully centralized system that budgeted at the end of some given period would involve delays no different from those in a fully decentralized system using the same budgeting period for batch decision-making. Although the two systems might select different projects from a given input of proposals, action on the proposals selected could begin at the same time in either case. It may be interesting to note, however, that as the budget period is changed, the advantage of investment results in favor of the centralized design may also change. Suppose, for example, we return to the first model developed in this chapter. Assume that the funds available for investment are proportional to the length of the budget period and that the number of proposals available for consideration is also proportional to the length of the budget period. Extending the budget period will then be analagous to expanding the scale of operations of the firm. As has been suggested, when this is done the advantage in favor of centralization tends to increase. Thus under these assumptions one might expect that, as the length of the budget period is increased, the difference in investment results will increase in favor of the centralized system.

Under the assumptions defining the "second model" above, the advantage does not depend on the scale of operations of the firm, and thus, in similar fashion, the advantage would not depend on the length of the budget period.

The divisions, in a decentralized design, might elect to budget more frequently, thus hoping to overcome through reduced delay the disadvantage they suffer in investment results. By using the second model, this possibility might be explored. Suppose a decentralized design in which budgeting occurs g times per year at regular intervals is to be compared with a centralized design that budgets once each year. In the former design assume that λ/g = mean number of proposals available for a budget at each division, and B/dg = funds available on each budgeting occasion at each division. Thus the investment results for each occasion are

$$\bar{Z}_{DC}(g) = d\left\{\frac{Bb}{dg} - (b-a)\frac{\left(\dfrac{B}{gd}\right)\left(\dfrac{B}{gd}+E(x)\right)}{2\dfrac{\lambda}{g}E(x)}\right\}.$$

We wish now to compare the present worths of the results achieved by the two designs at a given point in time, say, at the end of the year. If the results at the ends of the year for the decentralized design have a present worth of g times $\bar{Z}_{DC}(g)$, only further disadvantage will result from more frequent budgeting. If, however, the end-of-year present worth is, say, $g+K$ times $\bar{Z}_{DC}(g)$, some advantage appears. For example, if $g=12$ and i is the monthly compound interest rate, then

$$g + K = \sum_{j=0}^{11}(1+i)^j$$

or in simple interest terms

$$g + K = \sum_{j=0}^{11}(1+ji).$$

To see how large the effect of delays must be in order to make decentralized results equal those of a centralized design, we may set

$$\bar{Z}_C = (g+K)\bar{Z}_{DC}(g)$$

and solve for K . The result is

$$K = \frac{(b-a)\dfrac{gd-1}{2d\lambda}}{\dfrac{1}{g}\left\{b - (b-a)\dfrac{B+gdE(x)}{2d\lambda E(x)}\right\}}.$$

As one might expect from previous results, the value of K required to make results from the two designs equal (1) increases as the frequency of budgeting in the decentralized design increases; (2) decreases as the mean project size increases; and (3) decreases as the mean project flow rate increases.

It is interesting to note that in the decentralized design more frequent budgeting reduces delays yet decreases the selectivity of each budget and thus the investment results. One may thus find an optimal budgeting frequency for this design.

If the frequency of budgeting in the decentralized design is increased as much as possible, the divisions then operate on essentially a continuous budgeting policy. Hypotheses corresponding to the latter two above again appear. Some further comparisons between a decentralized continuous budgeting system and a centralized batch-budgeting system appear in Chapter VII.

Continuous Designs Compared

As we have seen, no difference in investment results would be expected between a centralized design and a decentralized one if both used policies of continuous budgeting. When delays are considered, it would appear that the centralized system suffers because of the time and effort required to communicate proposals to headquarters. If evaluation and decision times are the same for both systems and if there is little or no delay prior to decision in either system, this transmission time yields an advantage in favor of the decentralized design.

To assume that there is little or no delay prior to decision is to assume that there is no congestion of projects waiting for consideration. This implies that the resources available for processing the proposals are adequate to handle them as fast as they arise. Perhaps more likely is the situation in which decision-making capabilities are more limited and congestion of proposals does occur. It is natural to make a preliminary consideration of such a situation in terms of waiting-line theory. Indeed, the analysis of complementarities sketched in Chapter II is immediately useful here. If we consider the flows of proposals to be Poisson streams and the time required to make a decision on a given proposal to be random with a negative exponential probability distribution, some analagous hypotheses may be raised. If decision-making capability is measured by the mean rate at which decision can be made, one may compare centralized and decentralized designs with the same total capability. If the two systems have equal total proposal generation rates, the utilization of the decision capability will be the same in either design. The average delay prior to decision would, however, be less in the centralized design, another instance of the complementarity previously outlined.[5] Thus it is at least possible that the reduced delay prior to decision (congestion) appearing in the centralized design may compensate for the increased time required for the transmission of proposals, turning the advantage again to centralization.

1. For further discussion see Chapter II.

2. In discussing continuous budgeting, we have generally neglected discounting within the budget period in stating present worth.

3. Further comments on such approximations appear in Chapter VII.

4. Budgeting when a fixed number of projects are available raises some complexities of definition and analysis that have not been further discussed in what follows.

5. For the decentralized design one may compute the optimal allocation of a fixed quantity of decision-making resources among divisions with differing project generation rates in order to minimize the total delay.

CHAPTER 7

SIZE-GATE SYSTEMS

Size-gate Policies and Objectives

There is, as has been suggested, considerable evidence that firms elect to deal with the problems of decentralization in capital budgeting by permitting decisions on "small" projects to be made at lower organizational levels, but that large projects must be reviewed at higher levels. For example, in one organization proposals calling for an initial investment of $25,000 can be decided upon by a division manager, whereas proposals requiring larger initial investment must be sent to the corporate headquarters group. Indeed, in some firms there are several such levels of delegation specifying various sizes of projects that may be undertaken at the discretion of decision-makers at various levels. Such systems lead immediately to the questions of why a particular amount such as $25,000 was chosen, why the size of the initial investment is an effective basis for defining the degree of decentralization, and what would happen if this amount were changed.

We have called such systems "size-gate systems" to indicate that the flow of proposals to decision-makers is regulated by a gate that distinguishes among projects of different initial investments or sizes. We shall think of such a gate as being characterized by a gate value of the size of the initial investment that defines the distinction. Thus the size-gate might separate large from small projects using a gate value of $25,000 as the basis for separation. In particular, we shall consider size-gate systems that permit the operating divisions to make investments without further consultation with the headquarters group as long as the initial investment required is less than the gate value. In the case of larger investments the decision can only be made by headquarters.

The motivations for such systems include:

1. Regulating work loads at both levels of the organization

2. Maintaining control of the major directions of investment at head-quarters

3. Permitting headquarters to take advantage of ranking effects

4. Allowing the divisions to carry out small investments that
   a) Do not greatly influence the over-all directions of company investment

   b) Would ordinarily be approved by headquarters if referred, and thus gain nothing from the additional delay involved in referral

5. Attempting, roughly at least, to get the decision made at the level at which the best judgment and experience are available

Some Design Problems

The basic question in size-gate systems is clearly that of the effects of altering the gate value. From various points of view what can be said about the effectiveness of different gate values? Although the gate value might be changed from time to time—say, in response to changes in the flow of funds available to the firm—we shall assume that the designer is interested in gate values that will be changed only rarely. This appears to be in accordance with the stability of gate values observed in systems of this sort.

Different classes of projects, such as replacement, cost reduction, or expansion, and new product proposals, may be handled by different meth-ods in the firm. For example, as standardized methods of analyzing particu-lar classes of investments are developed, the gate values for these classes may be increased. This is in part a reflection of the fact that standardized methods of investment analysis tend to standardize the level of uncertainty associated with a class of projects by fixing the amount of information obtained. If the headquarters group can effectively communicate to the divisions the decision processes it would use in such standardized situations, the divisions become increasingly capable of reproducing the head-quarters choices, and thus the gate value may be increased with little change in the resulting investment action. In other words, as the probability of headquarters' confirming a divisional decision increases, the gate value tends to be increased. It is most important to note the difference between divisional ability to reproduce headquarters decisions and divisional motivation to do so.

Headquarters may establish a single gate value for all divisions, or this may be taken to depend on, say, the opportunity environment in which the division is searching. A division may also be restricted as to the total investment it may make in small projects during the budget period; that is, in addition to the gate value there may be a divisional budget restriction. Headquarters may permit the divisions to regulate their level of search effort, or this may be dictated to them. We may assume either that search effort for large and small projects can be controlled independently or that a single decision as to search effort produces some mix of large and small projects. Similarly, the amount of evaluation effort may be determined by headquarters or by the divisions, or this may be taken to depend on the nature of the project. For example, divisions may be permitted to regulate the evaluation of small projects, but the policies for evaluating large projects are dictated by the central agency. The headquarters group may use batch or continuous budgeting, and the divisions, by direction or by their own election, may use batch or continuous budgeting. We may assume ample projects for the firm as a whole, for headquarters alone, or for the divisions alone. These are the basic types of design questions examined in this and the following chapter.

Size-gate-only Systems

A size-gate-only system is one in which headquarters makes no explicit statement to the divisions as to the total amount they may invest in small projects during the budget period. Thus the gate value becomes the essential feature of the delegation arrangements. In such systems it would be reasonable to expect that headquarters fixes the gate value so that the amount of investment by the divisions remains "small" in relation to the firm's total budget. Further, the divisions may understand implicitly that there is some rough limit on the amount they should commit. If headquarters retains control of the level of search effort or the interest rate used in calculating the present worths of proposals, it has these further means of controlling the total investment made by the divisions.

To explore the effect of the gate size itself, we shall assume that it is the only operational policy imposed on the division managers by headquarters, and thus the division managers are not constrained with respect to their total investment in "small" projects. We suppose that the divisions are searching for investment possibilities in roughly similar opportunity environments and that there is some agreement as to what constitutes acceptable and unacceptable proposals. Those that are unacceptable are simply discarded without further consideration.

The division managers in such a situation will find it effective to adopt a continuous budgeting policy; that is, as proposals are made that are both acceptable and below the gate value, they are funded immediately. There is no motive to accumulate proposals into batches and select the best few from many. At headquarters, however, proposals are accumulated until the end of a budget period, at which time it becomes clear what funds remain available after the divisions' commitments. The "large" proposals "batched" at headquarters are then funded in rank order until funds are exhausted.

Such a system is obviously intended to allow the divisions to move quickly on small projects, avoiding the delays of formal presentation and transmission to headquarters, often only for "rubber stamp" approval. The system also attempts to keep the headquarters group from becoming involved in a large number of small projects so that they may devote their attention to the larger proposals that help determine the over-all destiny of the firm.

In the next section some hypotheses are raised based on a model of a size-gate system. These hypotheses concern:

1. The distribution of capital funds and the system's investment results under a size-gate design

2. The effect on system results of changes in the level of search effort or proposal flow

3. The effect on system results of changing the gate value

4. Hypotheses about the effects of delays in making investment decisions

5. Hypotheses about the effect of increasing the number of divisions

In sections immediately following, the analysis leading to these hypotheses is given.

Some Hypotheses about Size-gate Systems

Below are several hypotheses that may offer some insight into the problems of designing size-gate systems. Although it is difficult to appreciate the logical motivation for these without the supporting analysis, the main point is to offer the reader an opportunity to check them against his own observation.

1. The average investment results achieved by the headquarters group (large projects) depend not only on the average amount committed by the divisions to small projects but also on the variance of the amount committed by the divisions. Thus one might predict that efforts to regularize the amount of investment in small projects by the divisions will increase the investment results achieved by the firm, even though the average amount committed by the divisions does not change.

2. As the gate value is increased, headquarters investment results will decrease, but divisional investment results will increase.

3. Under rather general assumptions one would predict that as gate value increases, headquarters results decrease faster than divisional results increase; thus the firm's results decrease. From the point of view of the firm's investment results the optimum gate value is zero. This represents complete centralization of the capital-budgeting function.

4. As gate value increases, system investment results decrease at an increasing rate. Thus when the gate value is small, the decline in system investment results also tends to be small. In one example the divisions were able to commit up to 10 per cent of the firm's capital budget with a sacrifice of about 4.3 per cent of the firm's investment performance under complete centralization. (See Table 2).

5. The greater the search effort expended by the firm (that is, the greater the number of investment proposals it generates), the more rapid is the decline in system investment performance with increasing gate value.

6. If the gate value is fixed and if the volume of investment proposals considered by the firm is increased, the firm's investment performance first increases and later decreases. Thus for a given gate value there is an optimal rate for project generation. If the process, then, of searching out investment proposals is a matter of policy in the firm, it may wish to consider the compatibility of its level of search effort with its delegation system.

7. As the gate value increases, the optimal volume of investment proposals decreases.

8. If the firm's supply of funds is fixed and if the gate value remains constant, increasing the number of divisions has the effect of increasing the flow rate of proposals. Thus as the number of divisions is increased, the system investment results may first in-

TABLE 2

GATE VALUE	PROJECT GENERATION RATE = 20			PROJECT GENERATION RATE = 50			PROJECT GENERATION RATE = 100		
	System Results	Per cent Decline	Division Share Per cent	System Results	Per cent Decline	Division Share Per cent	System Results	Per cent Decline	Division Share Per cent
$c = 0.00$	14.75	0.00	0.00	17.90	0.00	0.00	18.95	0.00	0.00
$c = .05$	14.73	.14	.50	17.81	.50	1.25	18.75	1.06	2.50
$c = .10$	14.68	.61	2.00	17.57	1.84	5.00	18.13	4.33	10.00
$c = .20$	14.53	1.49	8.00	16.56	7.49	20.00	15.58	18.78	40.00
$c = 1.00$	10.00	32.20	100.00	10.00	44.13	100.00	10.00	47.23	100.00

crease and then decrease. Under these conditions there may be an optimal size for the firm in terms of an optimal number of divisions.

9. If the firm's supply of capital and the number of proposals generated increase in proportion to the number of divisions, then

   a) The investment results achieved by the firm divided by the number of divisions increase as the number of divisions increases.

   b) The investment results per dollar of capital available to the firm increase as the number of divisions increases.

Thus we see economies of scale or complementarity. The complementarity occurs because of the relative reduction (relative to total funds or number of divisions) in the variance of the funds invested by the divisions as a group or the funds invested by headquarters. The effect of this complementarity, therefore, will be a function of the degree of correlation among the amounts invested by the divisions. This, of course, is the very sort of complementarity discussed in Chapter II. (There is also a lesser effect due to the broader horizon of choice given the headquarters group.)

Thus it appears that we have here a combination of two complementarities noted in Chapter II, a variance effect coupled with a horizon of choice effect.

These sorts of hypotheses suggest immediately that the advantages of a delegation system based on a size gate must be in other factors than investment results. Such advantages may include (1) the ability to act quickly and without the expense of formalized analysis on small projects; and (2) freedom for the headquarters group from the daily affairs of the divisions so that their full talents may be applied to the long-range plans of the firm. Though these sorts of advantages may be difficult to evaluate in fine quantitative terms, one can see what their order or magnitude must be if they are to overcome the disadvantages in terms of investment results.

Search and Evaluation

Divisions operating under a size-gate-only policy with no total budget limitation have little basis for determining search policy beyond balancing their own marginal gain from the discovery of additional small projects against the marginal cost of doing so. Although they may also try to consider "their share" of the large projects that are sent to headquarters and ultimately funded, they cannot effectively do this without knowledge of the headquarters budget, the opportunity environments of the other divisions, and the levels of search effort chosen by them. Thus there are reasons for centralizing the decision as to level of search effort.

Consider next the evaluation of those large projects submitted to headquarters by the divisions. The divisions have little basis for determining an evaluation policy for these projects, since, as in the case of search policy, they do not have the information necessary to make a reasonable estimate of the chances that a project will be funded. (Of course, in a stable situation they may be able to estimate this rather well on the basis of past experience.) Thus it would be difficult to delegate evaluation policy for large projects.

For the small projects funded by the division under the assumptions we have made, it is certain that such a project will be funded. Thus a division that has to "pay for" evaluation efforts would come to much the same conclusion on evaluating small projects as would headquarters. This policy might thus reasonably be delegated.

We may note here the importance of "charging" the divisions for any evaluation effort they control. In the case of small projects they may fund, if evaluation effort is "free" to them, they may expend a great deal of it in the process of separating acceptable from unacceptable projects. Thus their investment results will, in the long run, turn out to be rather good— possibly better than is justified in terms of the cost of evaluation to the firm. If the divisions are permitted to determine evaluation policy for the large projects submitted to headquarters, they may reasonably assume that the more completely evaluated (justified or supported) a project, the greater its chances of being funded. In their desire to have headquarters fund the projects they submit, each division may be led to devote more effort to evaluation than would otherwise be reasonable. Only if the division is charged for evaluation effort can the policy be reasonably delegated. For further discussion of the principles involved here, see Chapter IX.

Analysis of Size-gate Systems

We now turn to an outline of the analysis that led to the hypotheses raised above. The analysis rests heavily on the concepts developed in the previous chapters, but it may be helpful to restate some of the symbolism at this point.

Let

x = the size of a project

$f(x)$ = distribution of x

$p(c)$ = proportion of projects with an initial investment less than the gate value, c

λ = rate at which projects are generated by a division (assumed to be equal for both divisions)

$\bar{x}_c$ = average size of a project, given that its size is less than or equal to c

B = original capital funds available to headquarters (exclusive of funds for search)

$\bar{y}_c$ = expected size of a project, given that its size is greater than c

The following relations will be useful:

$$p(c) = \int_{x=0}^{c} f(x)dx$$

$$\bar{x}_c = \frac{1}{p(c)} \int_{x=0}^{c} xf(x)dx$$

$$\bar{y}_c = \frac{1}{1-p(c)} \int_{x=c}^{\infty} xf(x)dx$$

Consider a system in which there are two divisions and a headquarters group. Proposals are generated by each division in a Poisson manner at mean rate λ proposals per budget period. The total number of proposals generated by both divisions in a budget period is n, a Poisson random variable with mean $= 2\lambda$ and variance $\text{Var}(n) = 2\lambda$. The total investment in a budget period by both divisions is a random variable D. The expected value of D is given by

$$\bar{D} = 2\lambda p(c)\bar{x}_c .$$

The variance of D is [1]

$$\text{Var}(D) = 2\lambda p(c)\{\text{Var}(x|x \le c) + \bar{x}_c^2\} .$$

As the mean rate at which proposals are generated grows large, one might expect the distribution of D to approach the normal. The funds invested by headquarters under the assumption that projects are ample at headquarters amount to $B - D$. Since D is a random variable, the expected headquarters investment is also a random variable with mean $B - D$ and with variance given by

$$\text{Var}(B - D) = \text{Var}(D) .$$

Under the assumption of continuous budgeting by the divisions, their total investment result is given by

$$\bar{Z}_{\text{div}} = 2\lambda p(c)\bar{x}_c \bar{P}$$

where $\bar{P}$ is the expected value of the present worth per dollar invested. If we assume that the present worth per dollar invested is uniformly distributed over the range a to b,

$$\bar{P} = \frac{a+b}{2}.$$

For a *fixed* division investment D, headquarters investment result is given by

$$\bar{Z}_{hq} = (B - D)b - \frac{(B - D)(b - a)\left\{\dfrac{B - D}{\bar{y}_c} + 1\right\}}{4\lambda(1 - p(c))}.$$

(We continue the assumption that the present worth per dollar invested is uniformly distributed.) Since D is a random variable, we take the expected value of $\bar{Z}_{hq}$ with respect to D, obtaining

$$\bar{Z}_{hq} = (B - \bar{D})b - \frac{(b - a)\left\{\dfrac{E(B - D)^2}{\bar{y}_c} + B - D\right\}}{4\lambda(1 - p(c))}.$$

Since

$$E(B - D)^2 = \text{Var}(B - D) + (E(B - D))^2$$
$$= \text{Var } D + (B - \bar{D})^2,$$

it is evident that the greater the variance of the total division investment, the smaller the investment result achieved by headquarters.

It is clear that as the gate value is increased, the investment results achieved by the divisions $\bar{Z}_{div}$ increase. The divisions are able to fund more and larger projects. As the gate value increases, the investment results at headquarters $\bar{Z}_{hq}$ decreases. This may be seen by showing that under the assumption of ample projects at headquarters, the derivative of $\bar{Z}_{hq}$ with respect to c is negative. The derivative may be written

$$\frac{d\bar{Z}_{hq}}{dc} = -2\lambda cf(c)(b - a) - 2\lambda cf(c)a$$

$$+ (b - a)\left\{ \frac{cf(c)}{2(1 - p(c))} + \frac{cf(c)(B - \bar{D})}{\displaystyle\int_{x=c}^{\infty} xf(x)dx} + \text{negative terms} \right\}.$$

If the expression below is negative, the derivative above will also be negative.

$$(b - a)cf(c)\left\{-2\lambda + \frac{1}{2(1 - p(c))} + \frac{B - \overline{D}}{\displaystyle\int_{x=c}^{\infty} xf(x)dx}\right\}$$

$$= \frac{(b - a)cf(c)}{1 - p(c)}\left\{\frac{1}{2} - 2\lambda(1 - p(c)) + \frac{B - \overline{D}}{\overline{y}_c}\right\}.$$

Now: $B - \overline{D}/\overline{y}_c$ is the average number of projects funded by headquarters, and $2\lambda(1 - p(c))$ is the average number of projects submitted to headquarters. Since under the ample projects assumption the number of projects submitted is greater than the number funded, the expression is negative. Thus as the gate value is increased, one may expect headquarters investment results to decrease.

The next question is whether, as the gate value is increased, headquarters results decrease faster than divisional results increase. If this is so, system investment results clearly decrease as the gate value increases. This can be established by developing

$$\frac{d\overline{Z}_{hq}}{dc} + \frac{d\overline{Z}_{div}}{dc}$$

and showing, in a manner similar to that of the previous result, that the result must be negative under the assumption of ample projects at headquarters.

Optimal Level of Search Effort

If the gate value for a firm is taken to be fixed, it may be of some interest to explore its investment results as the level of search effort λ is varied. As the number of proposals generated by the firm increases from some small value, the investment results at first increase. This is the result of the increasing number of proposals from which headquarters may select, an effect that outweighs the increasing amount invested by the divisions. After some increase in the level of search effort, however, the amount invested by the divisions without selection begins to detract from the results obtainable at headquarters through greater selectivity. Thus there is an optimal rate at which the divisions should generate proposals if the firm wishes to maximize its investment results for a given gate value. Setting the derivative of the firm's investment results with respect to λ equal to zero and solving yields

$$\lambda = \sqrt{\frac{B(B + \bar{y}_c)}{4(1 - p(c))p(c)\bar{x}_c \left(\bar{y}_c + \dfrac{p(c)\bar{x}_c}{1 - p(c)} \right)}}$$

as the maximizing value of λ.

Increasing the Number of Divisions

Suppose a firm consists of a headquarters group and N operating divisions. Each division generates proposals at mean rate λ. To investigate the effects of expanding the firm through increasing the number of divisions, assume that the funds available to the firm are proportional to the number of divisions. Further suppose that the amount of investment by a division is a random variable that is independent of the amount invested by the other divisions. With this assumption the variance of the total amount invested by the divisions will be proportional to the number of divisions. If we let B_d = the amount invested by a division, the total average investment by N divisions may be written $N\bar{B}_d$, and the variance of the total divisional investment may be written $N\text{Var}(B_d)$. The total investment results achieved by the divisions will be proportional to N. The results achieved by headquarters may be expressed

$$\bar{Z}_{hq} = N(B - \bar{B}_d)b - (b - a) \frac{N\,\text{Var}(B_d) + N^2(B - \bar{B}d)^2 + N(B - \bar{B}d)\bar{y}_c}{4N\lambda(1 - p(c))y_c}.$$

This is of the form $\bar{Z}_{hq} = KN - k$. Thus it follows immediately that the investment results per division or the investment results per dollar invested tend to increase as the number of divisions increases. This complementarity will tend to be reduced if the amounts invested by the divisions are not independent.

An Example

To give some feeling of the behavior of size-gate systems, it may be useful to explore a numerical example. Suppose a firm has $10 million available for investment during a year. The firm's two divisions generate proposals requiring an initial investment uniformly distributed over the range 0 to $1 million. The present worth-per-dollar investment that characterizes the firm's opportunity environment is a uniformly distributed random variable over the range 0 to 2. Table 2 explores the effects of various gate values and project generation rates. In addition to system investment results, the table shows the percentage of decline in these results from those achievable with complete centralization, and the percentage of the firm's funds invested by the divisions.

This example suggests that as gate values are increased, the firm's results tend to decrease at an increasing rate. Further, the greater the project generation rate, the more rapid the decline in the firm's investment results as the gate value is increased.

The optimal values of the project generation rate λ for each division are shown in Table 3.

TABLE 3

Gate Value c	Optimal Project Generation Rate for a Division, λ
.05	205
.10	102
.20	50

Delay Effects

A rough idea of the advantages due to faster implementation that would make a partially decentralized system equivalent to a centralized one may be obtained in this example. Suppose, for example, that the decline in investment results due to partial decentralization is expressed as $\overline{Z}_c - \overline{Z}_{dc}$. If the amount invested by the divisions under partial decentralization $\overline{Z}_{\text{div}}$ has a future worth $k\overline{Z}_{\text{div}}$ at the end of the budget period, we may ask what the value of k must be for

$$\overline{Z}_c - \overline{Z}_{dc} = (1 - k)\overline{Z}_{\text{div}}.$$

If one assumes that the investments made on the basis of continuous budgeting by the divisions are uniformly distributed in time throughout the budget period, the average time advantage is one-half of the budget period, or six months in this example. If i is taken to be the annual interest rate on a simple interest basis, we may write $k = 1 + .5i$. In Table 4, the values of the simple interest rate are computed.

We cannot compare these interest rates with those being received by the firm without applying additional assumptions to the example. Roughly speaking, they may be regarded in some situations as good projects involving a high return. They may be considered essential projects in that the consequences of not undertaking them are serious, and thus both headquarters and the divisions will be agreed on their importance. In situations

TABLE 4

Gate Value c	Project Generation Rate	Simple Interest Rate, i
.05	20	80%
.10	20	70
.20	20	56
.05	50	144
.10	50	132
.20	50	130
.05	100	160
.10	100	164
.20	100	168

where such projects are not available, advantages due to reduced delay cannot be the sole justification for a policy of partial decentralization.

1. This follows from the result that if x_i and $(i = 1, \ldots n)$ are identically distributed random variables and

$$y = \sum_{i=1}^{n} x_i$$

where n is also a random variable, then $\text{Var}(y) = \bar{n}\text{Var}(x) + \bar{x}^2\text{Var}(n)$ where $\bar{n}$ and $\bar{x}$ are the respective means of n and x_i.

CHAPTER 8

SIZE-GATE AND DIVISIONAL BUDGET SYSTEMS

Adding a Divisional Budget Restriction

To the systems of partial decentralization examined in the previous chapter, we now add a new feature, the divisional budget restriction. As before, proposals generated by the divisions are classified into large and small projects according to the size of the initial investment required. An initial investment c called the gate value is used to distinguish the two classes of projects. We now add the restriction that a division may invest in small projects but only up to some total amount during a budget period. This divisional budget restriction becomes a significant new design parameter for the capital-budgeting system. Such systems, using both a size gate and a divisional budget restriction, appear to occur rather frequently. For example, nine of the forty-eight firms studied by Istvan used this sort of policy.[1] As we have previously mentioned, it is likely that even in systems where there exists no explicit divisional budget restriction, there is some form of implicit control of the total amount that the divisions will invest in small projects. This may be achieved through an informal understanding arising either out of the divisions' knowledge of the firm's current capital situation or out of established tradition. In the analysis that follows, the divisional budget restriction is made explicit, and efforts are made to explore the consequences of altering it. We shall continue some assumptions made previously and add others.

We continue to assume that divisions cannot independently control the generation of large and small projects. Large projects are submitted to headquarters, where a selection is made at the end of a budget period using a batch-budgeting policy. Both the divisions and the headquarters group are assumed to have ample projects; that is, each organization unit has more proposals than it can fund and thus may be selective in its budgeting. If the divisions are aware of the budget restrictions under which they work, they presumably elect a policy of batch budgeting in order to maximize their investment results. Since, however, they may find delay effects significant, we shall also examine the case in which continuous budgeting is done by the divisions.

The divisions will, under the ample projects assumption, arrive at the end of a budget period with more proposals for small projects than they can fund. Although these leftover proposals might be submitted to headquarters for consideration as possible inclusions in the budget, or kept over until a subsequent budget period, we shall assume otherwise. Considerable simplicity results from treating such leftover projects as being discarded at the end of the budget period. Size-gate and divisional budget systems have certain obvious attractions. They promise both the advantages and difficulties of partial decentralization examined in the previous chapter, with an additional reduction in the internal uncertainty experienced by the units. Each organizational unit presumably knows in advance the amount it will be able to invest. The divisions may be motivated to use batch budgeting, thus improving their investment results. It would seem reasonable that whatever policy is used to control search effort and project generation rates ought to be somewhat more effectively designed in the face of this added information. The headquarters group may benefit from the knowledge that a definite upper limit has been placed on the funds committed by the divisions, that definite plans may be made for its own budget, and that no rude surprises are likely to result from the investment activities of the divisions.

The design problems for such systems include the choice of

> Levels of search effort for the divisions
>
> Size of division budgets
>
> Gate value

so as to achieve good system performance. Note that if we take the gate value to be infinity and all funds are allocated to the divisions, we have the previously studied case of complete decentralization. If the gate value is zero and all funds are retained by headquarters, we have the case of complete centralization.

To begin the analysis, we shall assume that

a) The level of search effort carried on by the divisions is fixed and paid for out of funds not considered a part of the capital budget.

b) The size of the division budgets is fixed.

The problem, then, is to study the effects of various gate values, looking for a "best" value if such exists.

Some Hypotheses on Investment Results

We first state some hypotheses concerning the effects of gate values, divisional budgets, and levels of search effort on investment results. Following this, the way in which these hypotheses were obtained from the model are suggested, and a quantitative illustration is given.

1. As the gate value is increased, the investment results achieved by headquarters tend to decrease. This is to be expected, since the headquarters group must invest the same amount of money in projects selected from among a decreasing number of proposals.

2. The investment results achieved by a division increase as the gate value is increased if the division uses a policy of batch budgeting. The division has a larger list of proposals from which to choose as the gate value is increased, and thus can be more selective. (Hypotheses 3–6 below assume batch budgeting by the divisions.)

3. If headquarters and divisional budgets are fixed, system investment results first increase and then decrease as the gate value is raised. The optimal gate value is one that makes the ratio of number of projects funded to number of proposals considered approximately equal for each organizational unit.

4. If the number of proposals generated by the firm is large in relation to the funds available, the system's investment results are rather insensitive to gate-value and budget allocations as long as these are kept in the optimal relation indicated by the previous hypothesis. This, of course, suggests the means for achieving many of the advantages of partial decentralization without significant sacrifice in investment results.

5. To state the previous hypotheses somewhat differently: If the gate value is fixed, the optimal budget allocation is approximately one that makes the ratio of projects funded to proposals considered equal for each organizational unit. As before, the greater the number of projects considered by the firm in relation to the funds available, the less sensitive are

investment results to budget allocation as long as each unit funds roughly the same proportion of its proposals.

6. If we do not make approximations and keep budget allocations in optimal relation to gate values, the firm's investment results decrease as the gate value is increased.

   a) The greater the ratio of funds available to number of proposals considered by the firm, the greater the rate at which investment results decrease with increasing gate value. The "more ample" the number of proposals, the less costly a policy of partial decentralization.

   b) Investment results decrease more rapidly at first and then less rapidly with increasing gate value.

7. If the divisions use continuous budgeting, discarding any leftover projects, headquarters should retain funds sufficient to invest in about half of the proposals submitted to it. Remaining funds should be allocated to the divisions.

8. If the divisions use continuous budgeting and if headquarters has funds sufficient to invest in roughly half of the proposals submitted to it, system results decrease with increasing gate value somewhat faster than in the case of batch budgeting at the divisions.

Analysis of Size-gate and Divisional Budget Systems

As previously, we shall consider a firm consisting of a headquarters group and two divisions, although it is not difficult to generalize with respect to the number of divisions. We examine first the effects of altering the gate value.

In the previous discussion of projects of varying size, we established the following result: for any organizational unit with a budget of B and in which the number of projects considered in batch budgeting is a random variable with a Poisson distribution, the average investment results, assuming ample projects, is given by

$$\bar{Z} = Bb - \frac{B(b - a)(\bar{n}_B + 1)}{2\lambda T}$$

where $\bar{n}_B$ = average number of projects funded with a budget B.

To apply this result, we assume batch budgeting by both the divisions and by headquarters and that any projects left over after division funds are exhausted are simply discarded. Consider first the average investment results achieved by headquarters:

$\lambda(1 - p(c))$ = mean rate at which *each* division submits large projects to head-quarters

$2\lambda(1 - p(c))$ = total mean rate at which headquarters receives large projects

$B - 2D$ = funds remaining at headquarters after allocating an amount D to each division [2]

$\dfrac{B - 2D}{\bar{y}_c}$ = expected number of projects funded at headquarters (corresponds to $\bar{n}_B$ in the above form)

Thus the average investment results at headquarters is given by

$$\bar{Z}_{hq} = (B - 2D)b - \frac{(B - 2D)(b - a)\left\{\dfrac{B - 2D}{\bar{y}_c} + 1\right\}}{4\lambda T(1 - p(c))}.$$

We now consider the question of the effect on headquarters of results of changes in the gate value c. In particular, we study the first derivative of $\bar{Z}_{hq}$ with respect to c.

$$\frac{d\bar{Z}_{hq}}{dc} = \frac{(B - 2D)(b - a)}{4\lambda T(1 - p(c))^2}$$

$$\left\{(1 - p(c))\frac{d}{dc}\left(\frac{B - 2D}{\bar{y}_c} + 1\right) - \left(\frac{B - 2D}{\bar{y}_c} + 1\right)\frac{d}{dc}(1 - p(c))\right\}.$$

We now show that

$$\frac{d\bar{Z}_{hq}}{dc} \leq 0.$$

To see this, we first assume it to be true. This implies from the above relation that

$$\frac{(B - 2D)c\displaystyle\int_{x=c}^{\infty} f(x)dx}{\displaystyle\int_{x=c}^{\infty} xf(x)dx} + \frac{1}{\displaystyle\int_{x=c}^{\infty} f(x)dx} \geq 0.$$

Since both of the quantities must be positive, the inequality must hold and the assumption must be true. In other words, it appears quite generally true that the investment results achieved by headquarters tends to decrease as the gate value is increased. From the standpoint of headquarters alone, the gate value should be made small.

Next we investigate the effect of changing the gate value on the results achieved by the divisions. For a division the investment result is given by

$$\bar{Z}_{\text{div}} = Db - \frac{D(b-a)\left\{\dfrac{D}{\bar{x}_*}+1\right\}}{2\lambda Tp(c)}.$$

As before, we investigate the derivative of investment results with respect to c, the gate value.

$$\frac{d\bar{Z}_{\text{div}}}{dc} = -\frac{D(b-a)}{2\lambda T(p(c))^2}\left\{ Dp(c)\,\frac{f(c)\displaystyle\int_{x=0}^{c}xf(x)dx - cf(c)\displaystyle\int_{x=0}^{c}f(x)dx}{\left\{\displaystyle\int_{x=0}^{c}xf(x)dx\right\}^2}\right.$$

$$\left. -\left[D\,\frac{\displaystyle\int_{x=0}^{c}f(x)dx}{\displaystyle\int_{x=0}^{c}xf(x)dx}+1\right]f(c)\right\}.$$

If we assume that

$$\frac{d\bar{Z}_{\text{div}}}{dc} \geq 0,$$

the above reduces to

$$\frac{cD}{\left\{\displaystyle\int_{x=0}^{c}xf(x)dx\right\}^2}+1 \geq 0.$$

Since this inequality must hold, the assumption is proved. We can say, then, that the investment results achieved by the divisions tend to increase as the gate value is increased.

Optimal Gate Value

Consider the problem of finding the optimal gate value if the headquarters and divisional budgets are fixed. Using the results obtained in the previous section, we may set

$$\frac{d\bar{Z}_{\text{hq}}}{dc} + 2\frac{d\bar{Z}_{\text{div}}}{dc} = 0 .$$

Simplifying the resulting expression yields

$$\frac{B - 2D}{4(1 - p(c))^2}\left\{\frac{B - 2D}{\bar{y}_c^2} + \frac{1}{c}\right\} = \left\{\frac{D}{\bar{x}_c^2} + \frac{1}{c}\right\}\frac{D}{(p(c))^2} .$$

If we neglect the terms $1/c$, this may be reduced to

$$\frac{B - 2D}{2\lambda T(1 - p(c))\bar{y}_c} - = \frac{D}{\lambda Tp(c)\bar{x}_c}$$

which indicates that the ratio of the average number of projects funded by headquarters to the number of proposals examined at headquarters should be made equal to the same ratio for the divisions. Thus one might use as a rough approximation the policy of selecting a gate value so that the ratio of projects funded to projects considered is made equal for the various organizational units. This approximation is equivalent to assuming that

$$\bar{Z}_{\text{hq}} = (B - 2D)b - \frac{(b - a)(B - 2D)\left\{\dfrac{B - 2D}{\bar{y}_c} + 1\right\}}{4\lambda T(1 - p(c))}$$

may be approximated by

$$\bar{Z}_{\text{hq}} = (B - 2D)b - \frac{(b - a)(B - 2D)\left\{\dfrac{B - 2D}{\bar{y}_c}\right\}}{4\lambda T(1 - p(c))}$$

and similarly for divisional results. The larger the number of proposals considered in relation to the funds available at an organizational unit, the closer the approximation. Thus if we make the approximation in question, investment results are independent of gate value and budget allocation as long as these are kept in the optimal relation.

For a fully decentralized system with equal divisional budgets the approximation indicates that investment results will be unchanged from those of a fully centralized system. If we do not make the approximation, the difference in investment results between these two systems is

$$\bar{Z}_C - \bar{Z}_{DC} = (b - a)\frac{B}{4\lambda T} \cdot$$

Thus we see again that the greater the number of project proposals in relation to the funds available to the system, the smaller the difference above and thus the better the approximation.

Optimal Budget Allocations

Perhaps a more common problem in actual practice is that of making an optimal allocation of the funds available to the firm, given a fixed gate value. The gate value may be a matter of long-standing management policy to be changed with only the greatest reluctance. The problem then becomes one of allocating the varying amounts of funds that become available to the firm from budget period to budget period, in the face of an established gate size.

Let

$$\frac{d\bar{Z}_{hq}}{dB_H} = \frac{d\bar{Z}_{div}}{dB_D}$$

(B_H = headquarters budget and B_D = total divisional budget). The result may be simplified to

$$\frac{\dfrac{B_H}{\bar{y}_e} + \dfrac{1}{2}}{1 - p(c)} = \frac{\dfrac{B_D}{\bar{x}_e} + 1}{p(c)} \cdot$$

If we assume that this may be approximated by

$$\frac{B_H}{\bar{y}_e(1 - p(c))} = \frac{B_D}{\bar{x}_e p(c)},$$

the result indicated is similar to that obtained with the equivalent approximation in the previous section. For a given gate value, funds should be allocated so that the ratio of the number of projects funded to the number considered is the same for all organizational units. As in the previous section, we may then draw the conclusion that, with the approximation, investment results will not change with the degree of decentralization as long as gate value and budget allocation are kept in the optimal relation. To the extent that the approximation is applicable to a particular situation, it lends support to the convention that funds should be allocated to permit each organizational unit to fund the same proportion of its proposed projects. Alternatively, this may be stated in terms of allocating funds to units in proportion to the dollar value of the proposals they are considering.

If, however, we do not make the approximation, but rather for any gate value keep budget allocation in the relation given by

$$\frac{\frac{B_H}{\bar{y}_c} + \frac{1}{2}}{1 - p(c)} = \frac{\frac{B_D}{\bar{x}_c} + 1}{p(c)},$$

different results occur. It can be shown that if budget allocations satisfy the above relation for any gate value, then as the gate value is increased, investment results for the system tend to decrease. Investment results are greatest for a fully centralized system and decline to a minimum for a fully decentralized system. The greater the number of proposals generated by the system in relation to the funds available, the more moderate the rate at which systems results decline as the degree of decentralization is increased.

Continuous Budgeting at Divisions

Suppose that the divisions elect to budget continuously until their budget allocations are exhausted. Although this will not produce maximum investment results at divisional level, the importance of delays in undertaking projects may cause the divisions to act continuously. The system results will be

$$\bar{Z} = (B - 2D)b - (b - a)\frac{(B - 2D)\left\{\frac{B - 2D}{\bar{y}_c} + 1\right\}}{4\lambda T(1 - p(c))} + 2D\frac{b + a}{2}.$$

Suppose that gate value is fixed, and one wishes to allocate funds optimally in the face of the given gate value. If we let

$$\frac{d\bar{Z}_{hq}}{dB_H} = \frac{d\bar{Z}_{div}}{dB_D},$$

the result may be expressed as

$$B_H = \bar{y}_c\left\{\lambda T(1 - p(c)) + \frac{1}{2}\right\}.$$

Thus the funds retained at headquarters should be approximately equal to one-half of the value of the projects submitted to it. Alternatively, headquarters funds should be sufficient so that approximately one-half of the proposals submitted may be funded. If the firm does not have available sufficient funds to provide this amount at headquarters, all funds available should be retained by headquarters, leaving the divisions without budgets.

If funds are sufficient to provide headquarters with a budget at the level indicated above, as the gate value is increased with budgets in optimal relation to it, system results decrease. As the degree of decentralization increases, the investment results of the system approach those available from continuous budgeting. The rate of decline will be somewhat greater than in the case in which divisions are using batch budgeting.

One would generally expect that with continuous budgeting by the divisions and for a given gate value, a system utilizing an optimal division budget limitation would be more effective than a system without budget limitations. The budget limitation on the divisions reduces the variance of the amount they invest; and, as was seen in the previous chapter, this tends to increase system results. Furthermore, if no budget limitations are used, it will only be by chance that the divisions invest an optimal amount for a given gate value.

Delegation of Search Policy

If we continue the assumption that the generation of large and small projects cannot be controlled independently, we may be concerned with what would happen if divisions are permitted to control search efforts. Divisions may adopt a policy of discontinuing search when they have, under continuous budgeting, exhausted their budget allocations. This policy offers no assurance of producing an appropriate number of proposals for headquarters consideration.

Suppose, for example, divisions decide to choose in advance of a budget period a level of search effort that will, in the face of a given division budget and gate value, assure ample projects with some probability. If the marginal cost of increasing search effort above this level is less than the marginal increase in headquarters investment results at this level of search effort, the firm will gain by a higher level of search effort. Since the divisions do not consider the marginal gain at headquarters, they will not generally select an optimal level of search effort.

Several alternatives to the complete delegation of search decisions may be noted.

1. Full centralization may be used in which headquarters establishes search policy based on a fixed gate value, an optimal allocation of

funds based on gate value and level of search, and the marginal gain to the firm from increases in search effort.

2. Divisions may choose levels of search effort based not only on their own budgets but on their "share" of headquarters investment results. This requires that each division know the headquarters budget and the distribution of the number of projects submitted to headquarters by all other divisions.

3. Headquarters may "pay" a division for the proposals it submits, regulating the price to encourage the divisions to adopt a level of search effort optimal for the firm.

4. Headquarters may note that the level of search effort elected by the divisions is a function of the divisional budget allocations. Headquarters may thus attempt to use budget allocations to control not only the volume of divisional investment, but also the amount of search they choose. If we suppose, for example, that the level of search effort elected by the divisions is proportional to their budget allocations, the effectiveness of the system depends on the magnitude of the constant of proportionality. Under the assumption of continuous divisional budgeting the marginal gain to the firm from increasing divisional budgets (and thus the level of search effort) first increases and then decreases. If the funds available to the firm are small and the constant of proportionality is also small, this policy may indicate complete decentralization of both search and investment.

Some of these problems may be illustrated in the case where divisions use a policy of batch budgeting. In considering the general problem of matching search effort, gate value, and division budgets, it may be worth noting that the optimal gate value may be chosen without reference to the level of search effort employed by the divisions. This assumes, of course, that search is sufficient to support the assumption of ample projects for all organizational units.

System performance is given by

$$\bar{Z} = \bar{Z}_{hq} + 2\bar{Z}_{div}.$$

To choose c so as to maximize $\bar{Z}$, we would solve for c in the relation

$$\frac{d\bar{Z}}{dc} = \frac{d\bar{Z}_{hq}}{dc} + 2\frac{d\bar{Z}_{div}}{dc} = 0$$

The result is of the form

$$\frac{dZ}{dc} = -\frac{\alpha}{\lambda} + 2\frac{\beta}{\lambda} = 0$$

or $\alpha = 2\beta$. Thus the optimal value of c does not depend on the level of search effort.

In similar fashion it may be seen that the optimal divisional budget allocation does not depend on the level of search effort. In this respect batch budgeting at the divisions differs from continuous budgeting. In the latter instance the optimal division budget allocation does, as we have seen, depend on the level of search effort.

The interesting result appears to be, therefore, that the gate value may be chosen optimally (from the viewpoint of investment results) without reference to the level of search effort carried on by the divisions. This result assumes that

1. Division budget allocations are fixed.

2. Search effort does not go below the level that supports the assumption of ample projects.

3. Search funds do not come out of the capital budget.

4. Both headquarters and the divisions use batch budgeting.

5. The divisions discard projects which they cannot fund within their budget limitations.

6. The flows of large and small projects are not independently controlled.

We could imagine, therefore, the situation in which, if divisional budget allocations were fixed, one could first choose a gate value c and then choose a level of search effort that would be good in the face of the given budget allocations and the chosen gate value. We consider this problem next.

We continue the assumptions indicated above. Suppose first that a division wished to optimize its level of search effort in relation to the investment results from the small projects it is permitted to fund. Division performance is given by

$$\bar{Z}_{\text{div}} = Db - \frac{D(b-a)(\bar{n}_D + 1)}{2\lambda Tp(c)}.$$

The division would then be interested in the value of λ that satisfied the following relation.

$$\frac{d\bar{Z}_{\text{div}}}{d\lambda} = MC(\lambda) = \frac{1}{\lambda^2}\left\{\frac{D(b-a)(\bar{n}_D + 1)}{2Tp(c)}\right\}.$$

Here $MC(\lambda)$ is the marginal cost of search effort.

In the case where the marginal cost of search effort does not depend on λ, the solution is given by

$$\lambda = \sqrt{\frac{D(b-a)(\bar{n}_D + 1)}{2Tp(c)MC}}$$

where MC is simply the marginal cost of search effort.

Suppose next that headquarters wishes to direct the divisions to operate with a given level of search effort and to choose this level so as to be good from the viewpoint of the investment results achieved by headquarters. We assume that each division is to operate at the same level of search effort and that the cost of search is the same for each.

Headquarters will then be interested in the solution of

$$\frac{d\bar{Z}_{\mathrm{hq}}}{d\lambda} = 2MC(\lambda).$$

Again, if the marginal cost of search is independent of λ, this yields

$$\lambda = \sqrt{\frac{(B-2D)(b-a)(\bar{n}_B - 2D + 1)}{4\lambda T(1 - p(c))(2MC)}}.$$

Alternatively, headquarters might direct the divisions to operate at a specified level of search effort, based upon a consideration of the results achieved by the system as a whole. In this case headquarters would be interested in the solution of the relation

$$\frac{d\bar{Z}_{\mathrm{hq}}}{d\lambda} + 2\frac{d\bar{Z}_{\mathrm{div}}}{d\lambda} = 2MC(\lambda).$$

This latter case produces the best results, but of course it requires a centralized decision on the level of search effort. We now ask whether it is possible for headquarters to specify the gate value and division budget restrictions, but to leave to the divisions the choice of their levels of search effort in such a way as to achieve good results for the system as a whole. This is the prototype of many fundamental questions involved in the design of decentralized systems.

Suppose, first, that headquarters pays each division a fixed fee for each project submitted. Let r be the amount of this fee. A division seeking to maximize its expected profit would consider the quantity

$$\bar{Z}_{\mathrm{div}} + r\lambda T - C(\lambda)$$

where $C(\lambda)$ is the search cost for a given λ. The division will be interested in choosing the value of λ that satisfies the relation

$$\frac{d\bar{Z}_{\text{div}}}{d\lambda} + rT = MC(\lambda).$$

Thus it would appear that by a suitable choice of the fee r headquarters could motivate the divisions to adopt a level of search effort that would be optimal from the standpoint of the firm as a whole.

The fee r is essentially a transfer price or artificial market price used by headquarters as a mechanism for making the supply of projects match the requirement for them or the capital budget available. More will be said of this sort of price in Chapter IX. Note that a division need not know the amount of money available to the firm as a whole, the amount allocated to any other division, or the costs or level of search at any other division.

An alternative method for decentralizing decisions affecting the level of search effort might proceed as follows: Suppose any project funded by headquarters is considered a part of the investment results of the division that submitted it. This is the common case in which a division receiving funds from headquarters to undertake a large project considers the funds part of its own investment base and the revenues from the project part of its divisional revenues. For the sake of simplicity we assume that

1. All projects funded are considered to be undertaken by the division submitting them. Headquarters does not make investments itself but merely decides about the large projects submitted by the divisions.

2. A division's share in the number of projects funded by headquarters will be equal to the proportion of all projects submitted that come from the divisions; that is, if $\lambda_j =$ the mean search rate at division j, then the average number of division j projects that are funded by headquarters is

$$\frac{\lambda_j}{\lambda_1 + \lambda_2}(\bar{n}_{B} - {}_2D)$$

and the expected present worth for division j is

$$\frac{\lambda_j}{\lambda_1 + \lambda_2}\bar{Z}_{\text{hq}}.$$

This is to assume that the divisions are searching in identical opportunity environments and that the projects submitted by one division are not consistently better than those submitted by the other.

Now let the present worth of the division j projects funded by headquarters be symbolized by

$$\bar{Z}_{\text{hq}}(j,\lambda_1,\lambda_2) = \frac{\lambda_j}{\lambda_1 + \lambda_2}\bar{Z}_{\text{hq}}.$$

If search costs are the same for each division, each will wish to choose its level of search effort so as to satisfy

$$\frac{d\bar{Z}_{hq}(j,\lambda_1,\lambda_2)}{d\lambda_j} + \frac{d\bar{Z}_{div}}{d\lambda_j} = MC(\lambda_j) .$$

An equilibrium would exist if the values of λ_1 and λ_2 satisfied the pair of simultaneous equations obtained by letting $j = 1$ and 2 in the above expression. If search costs are equal and opportunity environments are identical, the solution will be the same as that for the case of a centrally determined policy. Thus this method of decentralization would produce (at equilibrium) the same results as the completely decentralized solution.

It should be noted, however, that if the system were to reach equilibrium immediately:

1. Headquarters would have to advise the divisions of the total amount of money available to the firm, an announcement that in practice the headquarters group is often reluctant to make.

2. The divisions would have to select their levels of search effort co-operatively so that each would be aware of the other's choice.

The problem at this point seems to have the structure of the type of profit-sharing problem discussed in Chapter IX. There exists an equilibrium point at which each division, by maximizing its own investment results, succeeds in maximizing investment results for the firm. The remaining practical question is whether the advantages of delegating search decisions would warrant the trial-and-error process by which the divisions might reach the equilibrium point.

Evaluation

The remarks made previously in discussing evaluation in partially decentralized systems based on both size and present worth per dollar are to a large extent relevant to the problem of delegating the evaluation function in size-gate and divisional budget systems.

If search and divisional budgets are fixed, a given division may estimate the probability that it will be able to fund a small project and plan evaluation effort accordingly. A similar conclusion would be arrived at by the headquarters group, and thus the decision may be decentralized. In the case of large projects, however, the divisions presumably lack knowledge of the funds available at headquarters or the opportunity environments of the other divisions as well as their search policies. Thus a division has little basis for estimating the probability that a given large project will be funded. This decision may well be left in the control of the headquarters group.

Changing the Number of Divisions

Suppose the firm expands, increasing the number of its divisions. Each new division generates proposals at the same average rate and is given a divisional budget equal to that of the other divisions. In addition, the headquarters budget increases in direct proportion to the number of divisions. It may be shown directly that the investment results per division or the investment results per dollar invested tend to increase as the number of divisions increases. Thus, as in the case of size-gate-only systems, there is a complementarity effect or economies of scale. It is a relatively minor effect in this case, however, being due to small improvements in the investment results achieved by headquarters.

If the funds available to the firm are held constant and the total amount allocated to the divisions is fixed, as the number of divisions is increased, the investment results achieved by the firm will decline. This assumes that the total number of proposals generated by the firm is independent of the number of divisions. If, on the other hand, the number of proposals increases in proportion to the number of divisions, the firm will benefit from expanding the number of divisions in the face of fixed budget totals.

An Example

By way of a quantitative illustration, we consider a firm with a total budget of $10 million available for investment during a year. The firm's two divisions generate proposals that require an initial investment that is uniformly distributed over the range $1 to $2 million and use a batch-budgeting policy. The present worth per dollar invested for these projects is uniformly distributed over the range 1 to 2. The number of projects generated by each division in a year is a Poisson-distributed random variable with a mean of 20 projects. Table 5 indicates the investment results for various division budget allocations and gate values.

The data show the optimal gate value for a given division budget and the way in which this changes as the degree of decentralization is increased. It is notable that the decline in investment results as the divisions budgets are increased is relatively small as long as optimal gate values are used. Thus the cost of decentralization may be moderate. For any given divisional budget allocation, the system's investment results are relatively flat in the neighborhood of the optimal gate value. Therefore, small changes in the gate value will not have large consequences. Similarly, for a given gate value the system's results may be relatively flat for variations in divisional budget allocation in the neighborhood of the optimal allocation.

TABLE 5

(All figures in millions of dollars)

GATE VALUE	DIVISION BUDGET, D							
	$1.0	1.4	1.8	2.2	2.6	3.0	3.4	3.8
$1.10	$18.34							
1.20	18.77							
1.30	18.85	18.79						
1.40	18.82	18.84	18.80	18.72				
1.50	18.71	18.78	18.82	18.80	18.75			
1.60		18.63	18.73	18.79	18.80	18.77	18.70	
1.70					18.74	18.78	18.78	18.73
1.80					18.48	18.63	18.73	18.78
1.90								18.57

1. Istvan, *op. cit.,* p. 21.

2. Note that the definition of D used here differs from that in the previous chapter. The symbol D now refers to the amount budgeted for *each* division, whereas previously it signified the investment by all divisions.

CHAPTER 9

TRANSFER PRICING AND PROFIT SHARING

Reviewing Design Objectives

One aim in the design of decentralized organizations is to create a decision-making system that produces as good (or nearly as good) results as centralized management, yet at the same time will achieve certain advantages. For example, one might seek a decentralized decision-making scheme that produces specific decisions comparing favorably with those made by centralized management and in addition yields advantages such as:

1. Reducing the need for co-ordination and the communication of specialized knowledge

2. Increasing incentives for subordinate decision-makers

3. Permitting decisions to be made by those best equipped to provide the necessary intuitive or judgmental inputs, and reducing the need to base decisions on readily communicable data

4. Achieving a more effective distribution of decision-making work load throughout the organization

5. Reducing delays in decision-making and implementation

6. Providing a better basis for the necessary trial-and-error process of management

7. Quickening the organization's reactions to changes in its environment

8. Widening the experience and training of executives coming up through the organization

9. Facilitating the comparison of subunits' effectiveness with other organizations having similar products or processes

10. Providing a basis for allocating capital and other resources controlled by headquarters among the subunits

11. Encouraging one subunit to share its specialized knowledge and skills with the others

Basic strategy involves forming organizational units that take advantage of complementarities, yet are self-contained to a large degree. Each of these units is then directed to pursue in a largely independent fashion its own objectives, with the hope that the resulting unit behavior will be good from the viewpoint of the organization as a whole. The fundamental problem is how to establish unit goals or objectives so that whatever interdependence exists will not lead to a serious impairment of one unit's effectiveness by the activities of another. Typically, organizational units or divisions are instructed and motivated to maximize the divisional profit or net worth. Ideally, one would like to find a method of defining and measuring divisional profit such that

1. If each division operates so as to maximize its divisional profit, the firm as a whole will find its profit maximized.

2. Each division may act without knowledge of, or concern for, the actions of other divisions.

3. The headquarters group, having motivated the divisions to maximize their individual profits, need devote little further attention to co-ordinating divisional activities.

As has been outlined in Chapter II, divisions may be interdependent in many ways. To the degree that such interdependence exists, the complete decentralization of the above ideal becomes difficult or impossible.

The basic issues may be illustrated with some simple examples. In the previous chapter a situation arose in which, having told the divisions to maximize their investment results, headquarters actually wishes them to undertake more search than they find necessary from their own viewpoints.

The problem is to find a way of motivating the divisions to produce a number of proposals that will be optimal for the firm but not for the divisions individually. The headquarters group might well seek some means of doing this short of actually dictating search policy. One way to do this is to "pay" the divisions for the proposals they submit.

Transfer Pricing

Suppose there are two divisions that are motivated to maximize their divisional profits, and an output of one is an input of the other. This transfer of goods, services, or information may be conducted as a sale by establishing a transfer price as an accounting device for computing divisional profits. Hopefully, the transfer price would operate as does the price system in an idealized economy, using the mechanism of a free market to bring about co-ordination of supply and demand. Indeed, an ideal transfer-price system might involve simply the announcement by headquarters that divisions will be rewarded in proportion to their divisional profits and that transfers will be made at prices freely negotiated by the divisions. If such a system could quickly bring about the co-ordination of divisional inputs and outputs at levels that would result in profit maximization for the firm, headquarters would be virtually relieved of the burdens of co-ordination and control.

Although transfer pricing is widely used in practice, few suppose that it can fully succeed in this degree of decentralization. Yet with all the imperfections that arise through the complex interdependencies of actual divisionalized firms, the system does appear to contribute importantly to the degree of decentralization effectively achieved.

An Example

To emphasize the fundamental design problem, we will consider first a firm in which divisions are interdependent in input-output relationships, but in no other way. In subsequent sections the problems of more complex interdependence will be suggested. In particular, consider a firm in which one division, called the production division, furnishes an output that forms the input of a second division, called the sales division. The sales division, with or without further processing, sells the resulting product. To make the problem simple, we suppose that the units of measurement for the output of the production division are the same as those of the units in which sales are made. The production division is not permitted to sell its output to anyone other than the sales division, nor is the sales division permitted to buy its input elsewhere.[1] By implication, this means we are not concerned with closing down the production division and relying on an outside supplier, nor are we concerned with closing the selling division in favor of an outside sales organization. This has the further implication that in the price-quantity decisions to be considered, we need not be concerned with fixed costs incurred anywhere in the firm.

The firm also has a headquarters group, and the basic question is the degree of control that should be maintained by this group. Suppose first that the headquarters group elects to maintain full control of the firm's operations. It wishes to manage the firm so as to maximize its profit. We suppose that there are strong economic reasons why the quantity produced by the production division should be made equal to the quantity sold by the sales division. For example, imbalances yielding positive intermediate inventory may be costly because of high storage, spoilage, or obsolescence costs. Imbalances yielding negative intermediate inventories may result in lost sales, loss of customer good will, or necessitate costly emergency action. Thus there is a basic problem of co-ordinating the activities of the two divisions, which headquarters elects to solve through centralized control.

The headquarters group then requires the production division to report cost information indicating the cost of production at various levels of activity. The production cost of D units may be represented by the function $TC_p(D)$. Similarly, the sales department is required to supply information on the cost of selling D units $TC_s(D)$ and the revenue to the firm from such sales $TR(D)$. Obviously, this data will often be a matter of considerable uncertainty and be changing more or less rapidly with time. However, we suppress these realistic considerations in order to illustrate some points about organizational design.

The headquarters group then considers the profit to the firm at various levels of activity $PR(D)$ and chooses a program of production and sales that will maximize this.

$$PR(D) = TR(D) - TC_s(D) - TC_p(D).$$

If we make the conventional assumptions about the form of this function, profit will be maximized when [2]

$$\frac{dPR(D)}{dD} = 0 = MR(D) - MC_s(D) - MC_p(D)$$

where the quantities on the right-hand side are the marginal revenue, marginal selling cost, and marginal production costs respectively. This is the conventional doctrine of setting marginal cost equal to marginal revenue in order to maximize profit. Headquarters now informs the production division of the quantity to be produced and the sales division of the quantity to be sold. The sales division presumably takes whatever action is appropriate to achieve this result, adjusting sales effort or price, or both.

Consider now an example of a decentralized plan of operation for the firm. The divisions are instructed to maximize their divisional profits. The selling division pays a price p to the production division for the material transferred between the two. If this price is chosen correctly, the resulting program of production and sales will be the same as that obtained by the centralized plan. The production division computes its divisional profit as $pD - TC_p(D)$ and maximizes it by choosing D so as to make $MC_p(D) = p$. The sales division in similar fashion chooses D so as to make $MR(D) = MC_s(D) + p$. Now if the transfer price p has been chosen equal to $MR(D_0) - MC_s(D_0) = MC_p(D_0)$, both divisions will adopt the same level of operation, and this level will be optimal for the firm. Thus the selection of the appropriate transfer price "solves" the problem of co-ordination among decentralized units, yet produces results equal to those under centralized operation.[3]

This basic plan, which might be called marginal-cost transfer pricing, presents at least two sorts of difficulties. The first is the question of how the transfer price is to be determined.[4] Clearly, headquarters might require the divisions to report cost and revenue information, compute the optimum transfer price, and simply announce it to them. Although this would require considerable information to be sent to headquarters, it would achieve whatever benefits there may be from letting the divisions choose their own level of activity. This indeed is the way some firms actually are operating, announcing transfer prices at which exchanges are to be made among their divisions. We shall shortly examine some alternate methods of obtaining the transfer price that require a little less centralization of knowledge.

The second sort of problem arises when the organization grows more complex and further interdependencies exist. Will the plan of marginal-cost transfer pricing remain as useful as in the simple case? Suppose we consider a firm that has two sales divisions, A and B. Now, if the two sales divisions operate in different markets, it may well be that price or quantity decisions made by division A have no effect on the revenue of division B. The same thing might be true if they sold quite different products. In this situation the marginal revenue that division A calculates in making its decisions will actually be the marginal revenue for the firm as a whole. Thus it will be considering the same marginal revenue that would be considered by head-quarters under central control, and the division's profit-maximization plans will be the same as those that would be determined centrally. Alternatively, suppose that the products are interdependent in the market. Sales of the product of division A may either complement or compete with sales from division B. If the products are substitutes or near-substitutes, the sales of one will tend to reduce the sales of the other. If the products are comple-mentary, the sales of one will tend to increase the sales of the other, as in the cases of equipment and spare parts, boats and outboard motors, or cameras and film. With such interdependence, division A really should consider the marginal revenue of division B as well as its own in making its price and volume decisions. A decentralized firm must provide some means beyond simply marginal-cost transfer pricing to achieve co-ordination in this case.

Obtaining the Transfer Price

In the firm with a production division and a sales division, with no outside purchases by the sales division and no outside sales by the production division, it has been suggested that the headquarters group might simply collect the information necessary to compute the transfer price and then announce it. An alternative plan might involve bringing together representatives of the two divisions who are required to negotiate under certain rules laid down by headquarters. Suppose that the production division knows its total cost function, but the sales division and headquarters do not. The sales division knows its own cost function and the total revenue function, but production and headquarters do not. The representatives, meeting together, might operate as follows. Production proposes a production volume chosen essentially at random or based on some sort of past experience. Sales is required to respond by stating the highest unit price it would pay for this production volume. Notice that this is not free bargaining since sales, as the only buyer, could increase its divisional profit by refusing to pay such a high price. This would, if permitted, lead to results that would not be optimal for the firm. Production then considers the price offered by sales and responds with the largest quantity it would be willing to produce at that price. This also must be enforced by headquarters because production, as the single supplier, could hold out for a higher price or restrict its volume of production. This, incidentally, is one of the appeals of permitting sales to buy its requirements on the open market.

The process of proposal and response continues, hopefully to a conclusion at which the production division agrees to produce a quantity at a price equal to the price the sales division is willing to offer for that quantity. At this point each division will, since it is attempting to maximize its profit, find its marginal costs and marginal revenues equal, and these in turn equal to the transfer price. We would thus have the same solution reached previously, optimizing the firm's profit and co-ordinating production and sales. Such a plan has certain advantages: each division needs only to have information concerning itself, and headquarters needs only to lay down the rules for the meeting of the representatives.

This plan raises questions as to the consequences of various methods of adjustment that might be used by the divisional representatives. That is, if production finds sales unwilling to pay the price it would require for a level of production it has proposed, what adjustment is used in making its next proposal? Presumably, the adjustment would be in the form of a reduction in the proposed level of production. However, if the reduction is small, it may take a very long time to reach agreement. On the other hand, if the production representative is given to making large adjustments, he may continually "overshoot" the point of agreement. Even worse, one can imagine methods of adjustment that, if adhered to, simply drive the parties further from agreement rather than closer to it. If one knew the cost and revenue functions and the rules of adjustment used by the representatives, one could predict something of how long it would take to reach agreement. This will be of even greater consequence when we consider the case in which the divisions have very limited knowledge of their cost and revenue functions, and thus must proceed by trial and error to learn from experience.

As an example, consider the case of a production division having a total cost function quadratic in D, and thus a linear marginal cost function. Similarly, suppose the net revenue function (total revenue less selling cost) for the sales division is also quadratic, yielding a marginal revenue function that is linear. The proposal of a production level and the response of an offer are taken to occur in a time period, followed by a similar proposal and response in a subsequent time period. Thus in time period t production proposes a level $D(t)$ and sales offers a price $p(t)$. In response to $p(t)$, production proposes a new level $D(t + 1)$, and so on.

Sales, receiving the proposal $D(t)$, computes the marginal revenue at this level and offers a price equal to the marginal revenue. Thus if

$$MR(D) = b - 2cD$$

then

$$MR(D(t)) = b - 2cD(t) = p(t).$$

Similarly, production sets marginal cost equal to the price offered by sales, and proposes the resulting level of output.

$$MC(D(t + 1)) = f + 2hD(t + 1) = p(t)$$

or

$$D(t + 1) = \frac{p(t)}{2h} - \frac{f}{2h}.$$

Thus with both divisions responding so as to maximize their divisional profits and with quadratic cost and revenue functions, the response functions shown above are linear. These functions may be solved for $D(t)$, yielding

$$D(t) = AD(t-1) + B$$

where

$$A = -\frac{c}{h} \quad \text{and} \quad B = -\frac{f}{2h} + \frac{b}{2h}.$$

If production makes a first proposal $D(0)$, the system's time path is as follows:

$$D(1) = AD(0) + B$$

$$D(2) = A^2 D(0) + B(1 + A)$$

$$D(3) = A^3 D(0) + B(1 + A + A^2)$$

. . . .

$$D(t) = A^t D(0) + B(1 + A + \ldots + A^{t-1})$$

The behavior of the system can be predicted to some extent. If A is negative, the system oscillates, alternating high and low values of production. If A is less than -1, these oscillations grow larger with time, and the system is unstable. If A is greater than -1 but less than zero, the oscillations grow smaller with time, the system is stable, and it approaches a limiting or equilibrium value. If A is greater than zero but less than 1, the system does not oscillate, and approaches an equilibrium. If A is greater than 1, the system grows steadily more divergent, yielding higher and higher production levels.

In our example the value of A is negative, so the system might be expected to oscillate. If the slope of the marginal revenue function $-2c$ is numerically less than the slope of the marginal cost curve $2h$, the system will converge to an equilibrium. If we suppose this to be the case, as t grows large $D(t)$ approaches a value D_e given by

$$D_e = \frac{B}{1-A} = \frac{b-f}{2(c+h)}.$$

Thus in this particular case the representatives of the two divisions, operating in a manner described by the linear response equations above, will eventually reach the same conclusion that a fully informed centralized management would reach.

A Second System

An alternative system of some interest is based on transfer prices tentatively announced by the headquarters group. It is again assumed that the divisions know their cost or revenue functions and are motivated to maximize their divisional profits. Headquarters announces a transfer price to the divisions, to which they respond. Production, setting its marginal cost equal to the transfer price, responds by indicating the volume of production it would elect at this price. Sales similarly indicates the volume it would buy from production at this price. If the quantity offered by production is greater than that sales is willing to buy, headquarters lowers the transfer price. In the opposite situation, headquarters raises the transfer price. Hopefully, headquarters would eventually discover a price at which the quantities elected by production and sales would be equal, and this would also be the optimal quantity from the viewpoint of the firm. For example, the price announced by headquarters at time t, $p(t)$, might depend on the price in the previous period $p(t - 1)$ and the difference between the quantities proposed by the two divisions:

$$p(t) = p(t - 1) + k(D_s(t - 1) - D_p(t - 1))$$

where the subscripts s and p denote the sales and production divisions respectively. If we assume linear marginal cost and marginal revenue functions, an analysis similar to that used for the previous system will show that there are indeed conditions under which this system will converge toward a result optimal for the firm.

Profit Sharing

In the first transfer-price scheme it may be presumed that once the optimal transfer price has been announced, the divisions will immediately calculate the volumes that will maximize their profits. The firm will thus immediately arrive at a profit-maximizing level of operation. We now consider, for comparison, a simple profit-sharing scheme for decentralization, which does not permit the immediate optimization of the transfer-price scheme. This profit-sharing plan suggests that at the end of an operating period, the profit actually made by the firm is computed. This profit is then associated with divisions by allocating a fixed proportion k to production, and the remaining proportion $1 - k$ to sales. $(0 < k < 1)$. With k fixed, divisional profit maximization will result in organizational profit maximization. Both divisions will elect to operate at a level D_0, thus maximizing their own profits and rewards as well as the firm's profit.

The dynamics of this plan present some interesting difficulties as well as some useful possibilities. Consider the evolution of the system beginning just after some traumatic experience, such as its creation or some radical change in the cost or revenue structure. Headquarters announces that there is to be a profit-sharing plan, but it need not reveal the k that has been chosen. The production division is assumed to know its total cost function, but need not reveal this to anyone else. The sales division is assumed to know the total revenue function, but need not reveal it to anyone else. We consider time to be divided into operating periods for the system.

We consider the case in which the firm carries no intermediate inventory. Production simply delivers its output to sales, which in turn takes whatever action is required to sell the exact amount delivered. In this case sales has no opportunity to influence the level of operation since it simply disposes of what production delivers. We could insist, however, that in equilibrium, sales must be well satisfied with the level of operation achieved. (Alternatively, sales might be given the dominant role.)

Let

D_t = volume of production in operating period t (t = 1, 2, . . .)

D_0 = optimal volume of production

S_t = sales volume in period t

Our assumption above assures that $D_t = S_t$ for all t. By *equilibrium* we mean the condition that $D_t = D_{t-1}$. If the organization is well designed, the equilibrium level of output is equal to the optimal level D_0.

At the outset production knows only its total cost function and has, therefore, no very interesting basis for selecting an initial level of production. However, some sort of choice must be made, so we shall let D_1 equal production for the first period. The sales department then sells this amount. Headquarters, which presumably carries on the actual receiving and disbursing functions, then computes the profit earned during the first period. It need not know the cost and revenue functions to do this. Divisional profits are then reported, with each division learning only its own profit. For production, the divisional profit is

$$k(TR(D_1) - TC(D_1)) = Pp(D_1)$$

and for sales, it is

$$(1 - k)(TR(D_1) - TC(D_1)) = Ps(D_1).$$

At the end of the first period production knows, in addition to its total revenue function, the profit it earned $Pp(D_1)$. The question is, What should production do next?

Several things might be noted about this plan. The instructions given the divisions by headquarters are not explicit guides to action as in the case of transfer pricing. We suppose that headquarters simply urges the divisions to maximize their divisional profit. In transfer pricing, however, the divisions are explicitly instructed to maximize their profits by using the transfer price as either marginal revenue or a component of marginal cost. Thus the announcement of a transfer price implies a response on the part of the divisions, whereas the announcement of a division's profit leaves the response very much in the hands of the division itself. In this sense headquarters provides less information and direction in a profit-sharing plan. Thus one might wish to consider the hypothesis that profit sharing will result in a slower convergence to optimal conditions than will transfer pricing.

Of the endless variety of things production might do, we are perhaps most interested in those things that have some aspect of reason about them. As in all ongoing management processes in the face of incomplete information, the production division must conduct an experimental program. We shall assume that production has no staff resources with which to conduct "laboratory" experiments, and thus must experiment with the business itself.

It seems reasonable to attribute to production a realization that if production level is an issue in the firm, it must be that production division profit is not a monotonic function. The actual response function that production wishes to understand is given by

$$Pp(D) = k(TR(D) - TC(D)) .$$

Below are several programs that production might follow:

1. An initial level of production D_1 might be selected at random. Then let $D_2 = D_1 + m$. If $Pp(D_2) > Pp(D_1)$, let $D_3 = D_2 + m$; otherwise, let $D_3 = D_1 - m$. The rate at which this process brings the system toward equilibrium depends on m and the initial selection of a production level.

2. Choose two rather "well-spaced" production levels. The resulting division profits then provide a basis for the following argument: Assume $D_1 < D_2$. If $Pp(D_1) < Pp(D_2)$, the next level should be chosen greater than D_2 ; otherwise, it should be chosen less than D_2 . And so on.

3. Choose three production levels. Advance the hypothesis that the division profit function is quadratic. Solve the equations below for a_0 , a_1 , and a_2 .

$$a_0 + a_1 D_1 + a_2 D_1^2 = Pp(D_1)$$

$$a_0 + a_1 D_2 + a_2 D_2^2 = Pp(D_2)$$

$$a_0 + a_1 D_3 + a_2 D_3^2 = Pp(D_3).$$

Then choose $D_4 = -a_1/2a_2$, and expect a divisional profit of $Pp(D_4) = a_0 + a_1 D_4 + a_2 D_4^2$.

Other programs might be studied, but these three suggest the nature of the problem. It may be noted at this point that we are assuming fixed cost and revenue functions and errorless accounting reports. The main point here is that although these experimental programs might have been carried out by headquarters, nothing would have been gained by this. Thus there is no reason not to decentralize them. We know (although no member of the organization we are studying knows) that

$$Pp(D_i) = k(TR(D_i) - TC(D_i)).$$

The choice of a production level by the production division either depends upon past choices or it does not. If it does not, no learning takes place, and there can be little objectivity in production's decision. If the choice of a production level does depend upon past choices, this dependence may be represented by the function

$$D_t = L(D_{t-1}, D_{t-2}, \ldots D_1).$$

We might then study the question, What sorts of L functions will yield stable, optimal equilibrium conditions for the organization? The following hypotheses might be raised in connection with the L function. The more past experience brought to bear upon the choice of D_t, the "better" that choice is likely to be. On the other hand, this increases the information-storage and computation costs incurred by production. Further, if we are dealing with a static, errorless system as we have supposed, the past information very quickly becomes redundant. In our example, if the production division *knew* that the system was errorless and static, any information beyond that obtained in the first four periods is redundant. If, however, there is no a priori knowledge that the system is static and errorless, additional information may be useful for continual testing of this hypothesis. If in fact the system is not static—that is, the cost and revenue functions are changing over time—then information from the remote past may not only be useless but actually misleading. In this case the choice might be best if based upon information of only one or two periods in the past.

To illustrate the investigation of an L function, consider the simplest form:

$$D_t = L(D_{t-1}).$$

Of the possible forms for the function in this case, the following might be a reasonable example. At the end of a period $t - 1$ production notes that its total income is $Pp(D_{t-1}) + TC(D_{t-1})$. Production might then reason that its total income per unit will be constant in the future. (This is equivalent to assuming it is selling at a constant transfer price.) Having adopted this notion, production then simply chooses to maximize its divisional profit by choosing a production level that will make its marginal cost equal to its marginal income. Since we have assumed that production knows its total cost function, it can presumably do this. If marginal cost is given by $f + 2h$, the result is

$$D_t = \frac{1}{2h}\left\{\frac{(Pp(D_{t-1}) + TC(D_{t-1})}{D_{t-1}} - f\right\}.$$

Now if the system is to "work," it must eventually reach an equilibrium where $D_t = D_{t-1}$, and, furthermore, this equilibrium level of output must be equal to D_0, the optimal level for the organization. If we insist that our profit-sharing plan be restricted to sensible values of k, namely $0 < k < 1$, the system will work under the following conditions:

a) There are no fixed costs of production included in the computation.

b) Headquarters has chosen a profit sharing plan in which $k = h/c + h$.

The first condition might be met by instructing production to disregard fixed costs for computational and operating-decision purposes. The second condition can only be met deliberately by giving headquarters knowledge of the total cost and total revenue functions, as well as knowledge of the

FIG. 1.—Stable profit-sharing system.

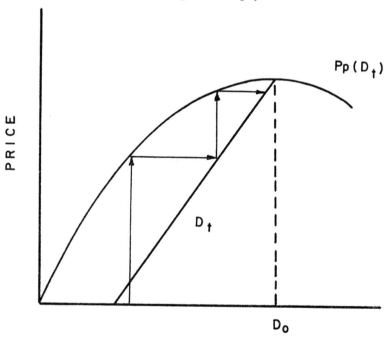

PRODUCTION

reasoning process to be used by production. Incidentally, this amounts to saying that the system will work if what production has assumed about it is true. To be slightly more general, consider any relation between D_t and D_{t-1} that involves the intervening quantity $Pp(D_{t-1})$, say,

$$D_t = L'(Pp(D_{t-1})).$$

The behavior of the system may be studied graphically by plotting the above function on the same graph as the function

$$Pp(D_t) = k(TR(D_t) - TC(D_t))$$

and letting all subscripts refer to the same point in time. (See Figure 1.)

For the system to have an optimal equilibrium, it must be that the two functions intersect at the optimal production level D_0. The equilibrium will be completely stable only if the function L' falls entirely below the divisional profit function, as in Figure 1. If the L' function falls above the divisional profit function in some range of D_t, the system is unstable in that range. (See Figure 2.)

Consider next the case of $D_t = L(D_{t-1}, D_{t-2})$. For example, suppose that production assumes the strongest thing it can assume on the basis of the data of two periods; namely, that the divisional income function is linear.

FIG. 2.—Unstable profit-sharing system.

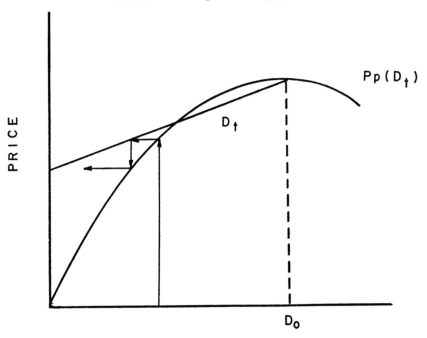

Production would then solve the following pair of equations for the co-efficients a_0 and a_1 .

$$a_0 + a_1 D_{t-1} = Pp(D_{t-1}) + TC(D_{t-1})$$

$$a_0 + a_1 D_{t-2} = Pp(D_{t-2}) + TC(D_{t-2})$$

On the basis of the resulting estimate of the divisional income function and knowledge of the total cost function, the maximum divisional profit output level may be computed. An investigation of this behavior shows that it will "work" if headquarters has chosen a profit-sharing plan for which $k = h/c + h$. This is condition b from above.

If production's behavior is of the form $D_t = L(D_{t-1}, D_{t-2}, D_{t-3})$, perhaps the most reasonable mode of choice is to solve the three equation systems presented previously. Here production will in fact obtain the divisional profit function directly, and it is not even necessary to know the total cost function.

Such simple views of the problems of organizational learning are, of course, complicated in reality by many additional considerations. The underlying relations may be complex, they may change with time, or there may be errors in the data gained from experience. In addition, there may be restrictions on the amount by which production, say, can vary its level of output without experiencing prohibitive expense. These are the problems of learning and control that confront any organization. These problems, how-ever, take on an added complexity for the firm attempting to decentralize in the face of interdependence or lack of self-containment among its divisions. Having examined divisions that are interdependent in an input-output relationship, we turn to the difficult problems arising from more complex forms of interdependence.

Cost and Demand Interdependence

A firm markets two products and is organized so that a division handles each product. If the two products are interdependent in their market behavior, their prices and sales volumes are interrelated. The products may be competitive in the sense of being substitutes or near substitutes for each other, or they may be complementary, the sales of one rising with the sales of the other. Thus the actions of one division have consequences for the results experienced by the other division. The critical question is whether, under a plan of decentralization, a division is motivated to con-sider the consequences of its actions for the other division and whether it can obtain information to act wisely if it does.

Suppose, for example, that the total revenue for the firm from sales D_1 units of product 1 and D_2 units of product 2 is given by

$$TR(D_1,D_2) = P_1D_1 + P_2D_2 .$$

If division 1 is concerned with selecting its sales volume, it presumably seeks to set its marginal cost equal to its marginal revenue. Interdependence implies that the price obtained for product 2 is a function of the volume of both products 1 and 2. Similarly, the price obtained for product 1 depends on the volumes of both products. The division's marginal revenue is

$$P_1 + D_1 \frac{\partial P_1}{\partial D_1} .$$

However, the marginal revenue for the firm is different:

$$\frac{\partial TR(D_1,D_2)}{\partial D_1} = P_1 + D_1 \frac{\partial P_1}{\partial D_1} + D_2 \frac{\partial P_2}{\partial D_1} .$$

The last term results from the interdependence between the two products. If we assume that the management of division 1 regards the first two terms as their divisional marginal revenue, a policy on their part of equating divisional marginal cost and revenue will not be optimal for the firm. To make a decision good for the firm, the management of division 1 would have to know, and be motivated to consider, these consequences relating to the other division.

In similar fashion, cost interdependence may exist between two production divisions. Division 1 may find that its marginal cost depends not only on its level of production but also on the level of production of product 2 by division 2. In turn, it may be that the level chosen by division 1 influences the marginal cost of division 2. Thus what a division may regard as its marginal cost may be quite different from the marginal cost for the firm. Since the "profit" of one division is influenced by actions of the other, it is difficult to form any concept of divisional profit useful for decentralization. If these two production divisions transfer their outputs to a sales division using a transfer-price mechanism, no single price for a product will suffice. A production division, using its own marginal cost for planning, would have to receive a price different from that paid by the sales division. The sales division would have to pay a price equal to the marginal cost for the firm as a whole if optimal sales decisions were to be made. Thus a transfer-price system would require some sort of intermediate agency that buys and sells at different prices.

Even aside from this difficulty, the complex process of organizational learning by which the divisions might reach an optimal solution appears discouragingly slow and costly. Consider the case of a single supplier and two sellers. If seller 1 decides to increase the price he offers the supplier for commodity 1 and if the marginal costs of production of commodities 1 and 2 are mutually dependent on their levels of production, then

1. This produces a change in the level of production of commodity 1 and a change in the amount of commodity 2 that the supplier is willing to furnish at the current transfer price; and

2. This, in turn, brings a response from the second seller that has its influence on the production of commodity 1 as well as on commodity 2, leading to an ultimate response from the first seller.

Thus the complex of adjustments is considerably greater than in the single supplier–single consumer case.

Profit sharing, on the other hand will work in the face of complex interdependence in the limited sense of supporting a solution that is optimal for the firm. That is, given that the firm was operating in an optimal way and given that the profit of each division was proportional to that of the firm, the divisions would have no motivation to alter their operating policies. Each division would find its own profit maximized, and simultaneously, that of the firm would be maximized. If the divisions do not know that they have reached the optimum point, their experimentation may lead to an unstable mode of operation for the firm as they test to see if improvements are possible. More serious, however, is the question of how such a profit-sharing firm would reach an optimal position in the first place. The process of trial-and-error adjustment would be no less complex and time-consuming than that suggested in the face of transfer pricing above.

Organizational Learning

The organization designer seeks fundamentally to create an adaptive system. Although an effective learning process is difficult enough to achieve in a centralized firm, it is even more difficult in a decentralized organization where the subunits are not fully self-contained. The basic criteria for any learning process are two. It should lead ultimately to a good result (in this case, operating policies optimal for the firm as a whole). Second, it should converge on this result quickly or economically. Though we have seen that transfer pricing under certain conditions, and profit sharing more generally, are satisfactory approaches to the first condition, neither promises economical convergence in the face of complex interdependence.

The manager of a decentralized division operating on a profit-sharing basis may be motivated to take actions that will improve the firm's profit, even if they seem detrimental to his own division; yet this requires that he be able to see beyond the bounds of his own unit. He may find that the operations of his unit are impaired by mistakes on the part of other units, and his best efforts may be negated by difficulties in the other divisions. Thus he must learn not only about his business environment, as every manager must, but about the interdependencies that exist among the units of his own firm. The complexity of this task and the inadequacy of his accounting system in the face of it may well suggest that his best operating hypothesis is to assume away all but the most obvious interdependencies and thus treat his unit as being more completely self-contained than is actually the case. This, of course, will result in something less than optimal decisions. The crucial question is thus whether the price paid for this lack of co-ordination outweighs the many advantages of decentralization.

Transfer Pricing and Profit Sharing in Practice

When a large divisionalized firm uses transfer pricing to compute divisional profits, it may not be primarily interested in the co-ordinative possibilities of such a plan. That is, the firm may not really expect the transfer price to bring about the best volume of transfers between divisions. In most cases it would appear that there are complex interdependencies that cannot be effectively co-ordinated with a simple transfer-price system. Indeed, it may well be that a "price" would have to be placed upon every activity of a division that interacts with the operations of another division. The time required for a transfer-price system to achieve co-ordination is also prohibitive. Many firms must react very quickly to changing market and inventory conditions—far too quickly to depend on the sort of trial-and-error process we have been exploring. Thus one is forced toward the hypothesis that in many firms the possible costs of lack of co-ordination or simply sluggish co-ordination are felt to be clearly greater than the costs of central control of some of the firm's operations.

What evolves in a firm is thus a system that occupies the middle ground between full centralization and full decentralization. In some activities where quick, positive co-ordination is important, central control is used. In some activities complementarities are achieved either by performing them centrally or by careful co-ordination. Since many of the ways in which the divisions are interdependent cannot be effectively evaluated in dollar terms, the headquarters group may keep track of a considerable profile of measures of divisional activity. The divisions thus find themselves constrained in many ways by policies laid down by headquarters, subject in many of their activities to direct co-ordination by headquarters and required to furnish a variety of information by means of which headquarters judges the effectiveness of its control. Yet within all these constraints, there remains to the division an area of autonomy. Centralization of authority is not complete, nor on the other hand is delegation. It is here that transfer pricing or profit sharing may play a useful role.

Their function is to provide incentives for the divisions to optimize the firm's objectives in those areas that are to some extent free of interdependence among divisions. For example, there may be many ways in which a producing division can reduce its costs that will in no important way influence the operations of the firm's other divisions. A scheme for computing division profit and for rewarding division management in proportion to their profit provides the motivating force for seeking these cost reductions. As long as the savings are realized in ways that do not react on other divisions, headquarters need not be aware of the details nor approve their undertaking. The major impact of divisional profit computations is thus to motivate management in the region of divisional self-containment. It is thus clear that an important task for the organizational designer is to determine the ways in which a unit is and is not self-contained.

Profit sharing on the other hand attempts a different sort of motivation. It tries to extend the attention of a division manager beyond the operations that are largely self-contained to the ways in which his actions most importantly influence other divisions. That is, profit sharing attempts to make division management aware of its interdependence, its lack of self-containment. Here, again, it is not generally supposed that profit sharing can be relied upon to bring about full, timely, and effective co-ordination among the divisions. Rather, it plays the role of attempting to motivate the divisions to preserve the co-ordination supplied by headquarters and to improve upon it where possible. This may be simply illustrated in the case of a trucking firm in which the terminal managers were rewarded for keeping their costs down. Each terminal manager's costs and profits were computed using, among other things, the direct labor costs of freight handling at his terminal only. Thus the terminal manager at A, in loading freight for transshipment at terminal B, was motivated to get the material on the trucks as quickly as possible, in whatever fashion, in order to keep down his handling costs. The effect, of course, was to raise the costs of handling at B, where considerable time was required to unload, sort, and check the freight.

Now, the simple announcement to terminal B's manager that he should load more carefully might be expected to have limited effectiveness in the face of his motivation for cost reduction. Instead, headquarters might bring about co-ordination by indicating an effective way of loading freight that would consider economies at both terminals. This then would be followed by a profit-sharing system in which the rewards for B's manager depended in part on the effectiveness of operations at terminal A. This would be aimed at motivating the manager at B to continue to use the co-ordinating plan developed by headquarters, and perhaps even to seek improvements in it.

---

1. Outside purchases and sales imply a competitive market for the commodity or service being transferred. Many firms use the "market price" as the transfer price in order to motivate divisions to operate at competitively efficient levels. Some firms

deliberately buy and sell a portion of the transferable commodities so as to keep the divisions aware of market levels.

2. For example, one might assume that profit is a quadratic function of volume.

3. If the firm's costs and revenues were linear functions of its level of production and sales, and if these activities were carried out subject to some linear constraints, the problem for the headquarters group has the form of a linear program. Under these conditions marginal costs and marginal revenues are constant within the range of feasible operations for the firm, and thus the transfer-price scheme as described here will not function. Interestingly enough, however, it is possible to obtain a set of prices that will permit decentralization. Roughly speaking, the production division need only know its costs and constraints, and the sales division need only have the same information about itself. Headquarters then announces a price and instructs the divisions to increase levels of activity if divisional profits are positive, decrease if negative, and maintain levels when divisional profits are zero. Headquarters, of course, must have rather full information on costs, revenues, and constraints in order to compute the appropriate prices.

Although such a system will maintain a decentralized optimum level of operation once achieved, it does not solve the problem of how to reach it. See, for example, Robert Dorfman, Paul Samuelson, and Robert Solow, *Linear Programming and Economic Analysis* (New York: McGraw-Hill, 1958); and T. C. Koopmans and Martin Beckmann, "Assignment Problems and the Location of Economic Activities," *Econometrica,* XXV, No. 1 (January, 1957), 53–76.

4. It is important to note that transfer price as determined here is not appropriate for many purposes. For example, divisional profit computed on the basis of the transfer price may not be a useful guide as to whether or not a division should be abandoned. If the transfer price is used to compute the value of inventories held by a division, this does not represent the actual investment by the firm in the inventories. Decisions about inventory policy made on the basis of the transfer may thus be misleading.

CHAPTER 10

PLANNING MANAGEMENT SYSTEMS

The Persistent Problem

One does not draw sharp conclusions from an exploratory discussion such as this. It is more realistic to aim rather at drawing attention to the problems of decentralization, to ways of looking at these problems, and to the possibilities for analytical and experimental approaches to them. It is not difficult to support the conclusion that these problems continue as prominent sources of organizational difficulty.[1] Governmental and industrial executives, meeting to explore the similarity of their organization problems, shared a concern over the degree of decentralization that could be effectively achieved. The main problem for both groups was the same: "Decentralization without abdication." [2] The development of the computer as the dominating influence in management systems has forced greater explicitness than ever before on the questions of management philosophy and methods of co-ordination. Few suppose that there will ever be a handbook for designers of management systems, yet the modest amount of research done so far suggests that useful contributions are possible.[3]

The Role of the Designer

It may be useful to view the complex process by which a large organization achieves its form as an evolutionary one. Evolution implies relatively small changes in the structure of the organization made from time to time. In the face of human limitations on the organizational planning process, and the considerable inertia of large organizations, small changes are the only ones ordinarily possible. Yet on occasion the organization reaches a critical point at which small changes appear insufficient. Then some powerful personality or group brings about a "reorganization" that changes the fundamental direction of evolution. Often, these reorganizations turn the firm toward greater centralization or decentralization. The elaboration of organizational changes is a complex process involving influence, personalities, and a persistent testing of the effectiveness of current arrangements.

It is difficult to foresee that a "designer" could bring order out of this seeming chaos. Yet someone directly concerned with the suggestion of alternate organizational forms, the exploration of their merits, and the conscious refinement of the evolutionary process might be influential in certain ways. For example, the concern of the designer might well be:

1. To suggest to management the potential advantages and disadvantages of various organizational forms and thus to avoid the assumption that a "reorganization" is called for in every major crisis. The designer may attempt to enhance the process by which management learns from experience, and thus avoid the unhappy phenomenon of "hunting" from one extreme of delegation to another.

2. To point out that the problem is non-trivial in the sense that good organizational designs appear to be neither those that are highly centralized nor highly decentralized. In this situation, analysis of the sort suggested here may serve to indicate the direction in which things will move as a result of altering the degree of centralization. If changes are to be small and their effects are not gross and obvious, intuition often needs the support of careful analysis.

3. To clarify for those in influential positions some of the concepts that appear to be useful in considering organizational plans. These might include the notions of complementarity, self-containment,

the definition of subunit goals, and so on. Most importantly, the designer may indicate to what extent these concepts can be made operational and thus subjects for careful staff study and analysis.

The efforts of designers to produce plans for management systems may typically be used, not as highly detailed guides, but rather as co-ordinative devices for the process of organizational change. The design may function as an explicit indicator of the direction in which the firm is moving and the sort of benefits to be expected. Although it does not spell out the maze of detail, it does provide a testing ground for the many small decisions that must be made. By this means the designer may bring some consistency to the process of organizational evolution, even though he cannot control it.

1. As this is written, several organizations are experiencing problems that can be at least partly understood in terms of centralization. Soviet Russia is moving away from central planning toward a free market, at least in consumer goods. Reports on the 1965 crises at the University of California point out excessive centralization. A new Secretary of Health, Education and Welfare confronts what some believe is excessive decentralization. The business press continues to report on companies that are either increasing or decreasing their degree of centralization to a notable extent.

2. A report of this Brookings Institution Conference appears in *Business Week,* August 7, 1965, pp. 84–86.

3. See, for example, K. J. Arrow, "Control in Large Organizations," *Management Science,* X, No. 3 (April, 1964), 397–408.

Bibliography

Although there is an extensive literature that is generally relevant to organizational problems, there are fewer discussions addressed directly to decentralization. Some of these are indicated below.

ALLEN, S. G. "Redistribution of Total Stock over Several User Locations," *Naval Research Logistics Quarterly,* V, No. 4 (December, 1958), 337–45.

BERMAN, E. B. "Monte Carlo Determination of Stock Redistribution," *Operations Research,* X (July, 1962), 500–506.

BIERMAN, H., JR. "Pricing Intracompany Transfers," *Accounting Review,* XXXIV (July, 1959), 429–32.

BROWN, WILFRED. *Exploration in Management.* New York: Wiley, 1960.

BURLINGAME, J. F. "Information Technology and Decentralization," *Harvard Business Review,* XXXIX (November–December, 1961), 121–26.

CHANDLER, A. D. *Strategy and Structure.* Cambridge: Massachusetts Institute of Technology Press, 1962.

CHARNES, A., and W. W. COOPER. "Management Models and Industrial Applications of Linear Programming," *Management Science,* IV, No. 1 (October, 1957), 38–87.

CLARK, A. J., and H. SCARF. "Optimal Policies for a Multi-echelon Inventory Problem," *Management Science,* VI, No. 4 (July, 1960), 475–90.

COCHRAN, THOMAS CHILDS. *Basic History of American Business.* Princeton, N.J.: Van Nostrand, 1959.

COOK, B. "Aeroquip Solves the Multi-plant Inventory Control Problem," *Purchasing,* XLVII (September 14, 1959), 87–89.

COOK, PAUL W., JR. "Decentralization and the Transfer Price Problem," *Journal of Business,* XXVIII, No. 2 (April, 1955), 87–94.

———. "New Technique for Intracompany Pricing," *Harvard Business Review*, XXXV, No. 4 (July–August, 1957), 74–80.

CORDINER, RALPH J. *New Frontiers for Professional Managers.* New York: McGraw-Hill, 1956.

CYERT, RICHARD M., and JAMES G. MARCH. *A Behavioral Theory of the Firm.* Englewood Cliffs, N.J.: Prentice-Hall, 1963.

DEAN, JOEL. *Managerial Economics.* New York: Prentice-Hall, 1951.

———. "Decentralized and Intracompany Pricing," *Harvard Business Review*, XXXIII, No. 4 (July–August, 1955), 65–74.

DEARDEN, JOHN. "Interdivisional Pricing," *Harvard Business Review*, XXXVIII, No. 1 (January–February, 1960), 117–25.

———. "Problem in Decentralized Profit Responsibility," *Harvard Business Review*, XXXVIII, No. 3 (May–June, 1960), 79–86.

———. Problem in Decentralized Financial Control," *Harvard Business Review*, XXXIX, No. 3 (May–June, 1961), 72–80.

DEARDEN, J. "Limits on Decentralized Profit Responsibility," *Harvard Business Review*, XL, No. 4 (July, 1962), 81–89.

DEARDEN, JOHN. "Mirage of Profit Decentralization," *Harvard Business Review*, XL, No. 6 (November–December, 1962).

DEVONS, ELY. *Planning in Practice.* Cambridge, Eng.: Cambridge University Press, 1950.

DORFMAN, ROBERT, PAUL SAMUELSON, and ROBERT SOLOW. *Linear Programming and Economic Analysis.* New York: McGraw-Hill, 1958.

DRUCKER, PETER. *The Concept of the Corporation.* New York: John Day Co., 1946.

FLORENCE, P. SARGENT. *The Logic of British and American Industry.* London: Routledge and Keegan Paul, 1953.

GILBERT, N. "How Rheem Finally Made Decentralization Work," *Sales Management*, LXXX (May 16, 1958), 33–35.

GILLIS, J. L. "When Is a Corporation Properly Decentralized?" *Commercial and Financial Chronicle*, CXCVI (October 4, 1962), 1413.

GOUGER, M. W. "Decentralization: Fact or Fancy," *Dun's Review and Modern Industry*, LXIX (May, 1957), 12.

GRANICK, DAVID. *The Red Executive.* Garden City, N.Y.: Doubleday, 1960.

GRAYSON, C. JACKSON, JR. *Decisions under Uncertainty: Drilling Decisions by Oil and Gas Operators.* Boston: Division of Research, Graduate School of Business Administration, Harvard University, 1960.

HABERSTROH, CHADWICK J. "Control As an Organizational Process," *Management Science*, VI, No. 2 (January, 1960), 165–71.

————. "Administration of Safety in the Steel Industry," *Management Science,* VII, No. 4 (July, 1961), 436–44.

HAIRE, MASON (ed.). *Modern Organization Theory: A Symposium.* New York: Wiley, 1959.

————. *Organization Theory in Industrial Practice: A Symposium.* New York: Wiley, 1962.

HANSSMANN, F. "Optimal Inventory Location and Control in Production and Distribution Networks," *Operations Research,* VII (July, 1959), 483–98.

HAYEK, FREDRICH AUGUST VON. *The Road to Serfdom.* Chicago: University of Chicago Press, 1944.

HAYNES, W. WARREN, and MARTIN B. SOLOMON. "A Misplaced Emphasis in Capital Budgeting," *Quarterly Review of Economics and Business,* II, No. 1 (February, 1962).

HELLER, WALTER H. "The Anatomy of Investment Decisions," *Harvard Business Review,* XXIX, No. 2 (March, 1951).

HENDERSON, D. E. "Centralized Control of Multiplant Operation: Some Benefits," *National Association of Accountants Bulletin,* XLIII (September, 1961), 92–93.

HILL, LAWRENCE S. "The Application of Queuing Theory to Span of Control," *Academy of Management Journal,* VI, No. 1 (March, 1963), 58–69.

HUGHES, L. M. "Localized Management Pays Off for Prudential," *Sales Management,* LXVIII (January 15, 1952), 24–27.

————. "General Electric under Decentralization," *Sales Management,* LXXX (March 7, 1958), 34–35.

KLINE, B. E., and N. H. MARTIN. "Freedom, Authority, and Decentralization," *Harvard Business Review,* XXXVI (May, 1958), 69–75.

KOOPMANS, T. C. *Three Essays on the State of Economic Science.* New York: McGraw-Hill, 1957.

KRUISINGA, H. J. (ed.). *The Balance between Centralization and Decentralization in Managerial Control.* Leiden: Kroese, 1954.

LASSWELL, HAROLD D. *Politics.* Cleveland, Ohio: Meridian Books, 1958.

LAWRENCE, PAUL R. *The Changing of Organizational Behavior Patterns.* Boston: Harvard University Graduate School of Business Administration, Division of Research, 1958.

LIKERT, RENSIS. "Measuring Organizational Performance," *Harvard Business Review,* XXXVI, No. 2 (March–April, 1958), 41–50.

MAGILL, F. R. "The Case for Decentralized Standardization," *American Business,* XXIX (February, 1959), 20–21.

MARCH, J. G., and H. A. SIMON. *Organizations.* New York: Wiley, 1958.

MARSCHAK, J. "Elements for a Theory of Teams," *Management Science,* I, No. 2 (January–March, 1955), 127–37.

MARSCHAK, THOMAS. "Centralization and Decentralization in Economic Organization," *Econometrica,* XXVII, No. 3 (July, 1959), 399–430.

McCREARY, E. "Top Management Tightens Controls: Countertrend to Decentralization," *Dun's Review and Modern Industry,* LXXIV (July, 1959), 32–34.

McGUIRE, C. B. "Some Team Models of a Sales Organization," *Management Science,* VII, No. 2 (January, 1961), 101–30.

MELLON, W. G. "A Selected Descriptive Bibliography of References on Priority Systems and Related Non-price Allocators," *Naval Research Logistics Quarterly,* V, No. 1 (March, 1958), 17–27.

MOBERG, H. W. "Principles of Control for Decentralized Operations," *National Association of Accountants Bulletin,* XLIII (July, 1962), 56.

MURPHY, ROBERT W. "Corporate Divisions vs. Subsidiaries," *Harvard Business Review,* XXXIV, No. 6 (November–December, 1956), 83–92.

PENROSE, E. T. *The Theory of the Growth of the Firm.* Oxford, Eng.: Blackwell, 1959.

PRUDENTIAL LIFE INSURANCE COMPANY. "Meeting Problems of Decentralization," *National Underwriter,* LVII (April 17, 1953), 2.

ROSS, A. D. "Management and the Size of the Firm," *Review of Economic Studies,* XIX (1951–52), 148–52.

RUBENSTEIN, ALBERT H. "Organizational Factors Affecting Research and Development Decision-making in Large Decentralized Companies," *Management Science,* X, No. 4 (July, 1964), 618–33.

SCHIEH, E. C. "Essence of Decentralization," *Advanced Management,* XXIV (September, 1959), 8–10.

SCHILLINGLAW, GORDON. "Guides to Internal Profit Measurement," *Harvard Business Review,* XXXV, No. 2 (March–April, 1957), 82–94.

SHUBIK, MARTIN. "Incentives, Decentralized Control, the Assignment of Joint Costs and Internal Pricing," *Management Science,* VIII, No. 3 (April, 1962), 325–43.

SIMPSON, K. F. "Theory of Allocation of Stocks to Warehouses," *Operations Research,* VII (November, 1959), 797–805.

SLOAN, ALFRED P., JR. *My Years with General Motors.* New York: Doubleday & Co., 1964.

SMITH, CALEB. "Survey of the Empirical Evidence on Economies of Scale," in *Business Concentration and Price Policy.* New York: Princeton

University Press for the National Bureau of Economic Research, 1955.

SMITH, GEORGE A., JR. *Managing Geographically Decentralized Companies.* Boston: Harvard University, Graduate School of Business Administration, Division of Research, 1958.

STRYKER, P. "Decentralizing of Blaw Knox," *Fortune,* LIII (February, 1956), 114–16.

SUOJANEN, W. W. "Substantive Decentralization in Large Corporations," *Advanced Management,* XXI (September, 1956), 16–22.

TRUNDLE, R. C. "Trends in Decentralization," *American Business,* XXV (December, 1955), 14–15.

UROW, HOWARD. "The Reorganization Controversy," *Journal of Industrial Engineering,* XI, No. 5 (September–October, 1960), 378–82.

VILLERS, RAYMOND. *The Dynamics of Industrial Management.* New York: Funk & Wagnalls Co., 1954.

———. "Control and Freedom in a Decentralized Company," *Harvard Business Review,* XXXII, No. 2 (March–April, 1954), 89–96.

VON MISES, LUDWIG. *Bureaucracy.* New Haven: Yale University Press, 1944.

WAGNER, HARVEY. "The Model of Financial Control in a Complex Organization," *Management Sciences Models and Techniques,* I. New York: Pergamon Press, 1960.

Index

Index